UNDER THREE FLAGS

UNDER THREE FLAGS

The Story of Gabriel Richard

by DAVID J. ABODAHER

ILLUSTRATED BY RICHARD LEWIS

Hawthorn Books, Inc.   **Publishers**   *New York*

FIRST PRINTING

H–9401

To
Father Edmund Schwager

with much gratitude for so much

CONTENTS

FAREWELL TO FRANCE

The darker gray of the twilight that comes just before night had already settled over the village of Honfleur. The four men—they were Frenchmen, but strangers to Honfleur—stood like four furtive black shadows looking out over the harbor.

The tall, gaunt one with a long, jagged scar across his jaw stood a few feet away from his three companions. After a moment he turned and looked up at the high hill which faced the river leading to the English Channel and freedom.

Far atop the hill he could see a small, simple cross silhouetted against the blackening sky. The rest of the historic Church of Notre Dame de Grace was blotted out by the dark and the trees which crested the hill.

The man with the scar on his jaw turned to the nearest of his friends. "Father . . ." he started to say. Then he stopped abruptly. He looked around quickly, as if hoping that nobody might have heard.

The others also looked from left to right, a momentary fear clouding their faces.

The man with the scar drew closer to his friend. "I'm sorry, François," he whispered. "For a moment, I forgot our danger."

The one addressed as François smiled sadly. "It is all right, Gabriel," he said softly. "No one is near and no harm has been done."

"It will be some hours before the tide is full, François," Gabriel said. "Perhaps, while we wait to board our ship, it would be safer in the church." He pointed to the cross above the domelike steeple of Notre Dame de Grace.

François' dark eyes followed the direction of Gabriel's hand. He turned to the others. They nodded and the four men moved silently toward the church.

Never since the days centuries past when sleek,

black Viking ships had moored in its harbor had such an ominous quiet hung over Honfleur. Even when part of the invasion fleet of William the Conqueror filled the harbor there had not been such tension and fear as now could be felt in the air itself.

True, since it was an important port, Honfleur had been the scene of much conflict. Yet many riotous, happy days had marked the history of the little village on the estuary of the Seine River.

For centuries, the men of Honfleur had set sail on fishing expeditions that took them as far west as the New World and the Gulf of St. Lawrence. Each return was accompanied by much celebrating on the cobbled streets.

Those same streets, too, had echoed to wild cheers as Richard the Lion-Hearted led his Crusaders through Honfleur on his way to battle the Saracens for the Holy Land.

Now Honfleur was deathly quiet. An air of danger stalked the cobbled streets as strangers stealthily made their way across them, and just as stealthily boarded boats that would carry them away to safety.

For this was the time of the Revolution in France. The time when no aristocrat and no priest or bishop was safe from the dreaded guillotine.

Hundreds of priests who refused to deny their first allegiance to God and accept the State as the last word for their beliefs and actions had already lost their heads to the plummeting ax. Others, lucky enough to escape arrest and trial, fled the country to spread God's word in new and strange lands.

Such were the four men who quietly made their way into the shadows of the Church of Notre Dame de Grace on that night after Easter in the year 1792.

Until nearly eleven o'clock that night, these four knelt in prayer in the darkened church. Now and then one of them would rise, go to the door of the church, cautiously push it open a few inches, and peer down into the now moonlit harbor. Finally, the hulking mass of a brigantine was seen in the water.

Silently, the man at the door returned to his kneeling companions and touched each on the shoulder. Silently, each rose to his feet, genuflected, and left the church. Silently, all four made their way to the harbor and boarded the waiting ship, *La Reine des Coeurs.*

No sooner had the last of the four set foot on the deck than the mooring lines were released and the sails unfurled. The brigantine moved out from the dock, away from the port of Honfleur and westward toward the English Channel.

On deck the four black-robed men looked through tear-filled eyes at the slowly fading shoreline of their homeland. It would be the last time most of them would ever see their beloved France.

The one with the scar across his jaw stood alone a few feet away from his companions. With a sigh, he lifted his eyes upward as if in prayer.

This was Father Gabriel Richard, like the others a Sulpician priest and, like the others, on his way to America.

Unlike the others, however, Gabriel Richard would be one remembered centuries later as a pioneer among pioneers in the wilderness of the New World.

CHAPTER 2

"A FAT AND HAPPY BOY"

Gabriel Richard was born in the French city of Saintes on October 15, 1767. His father, François, as well as his mother, Genevieve, came from titled families of Rochefort. François, who had been in the French naval service before his marriage, left the service and settled in Saintes with his wife.

François and Genevieve Richard were not of the aristocracy. Neither were they truly well to do. But they were of more than average means.

Before Gabriel was five years old, the father had moved his family from their first modest home in

14

Saintes to an estate of some hundred and fifty acres just outside the city. La Jallet, as the estate was known, was located in a beautiful area of dense woods and vineyards.

The house itself was not a luxurious or pretentious manor, but roomy and comfortable. It and its garden were surrounded by a high stone wall. Above the gate, inscribed in the masonry, were the words of the Psalmist: "Oh Lord, open Thou my mouth, and my tongue shall proclaim Thy righteousness and sing Thy praise."

Young Gabriel paid little attention to the inscription beneath which he walked daily. Yet it was to prove the great motivation of his life.

François and Genevieve Richard were strict but affectionate parents. Gabriel was an energetic and fun-loving boy, and his childhood years were happy ones.

Until he was twelve years of age, Gabriel was taught by a tutor. Then he was enrolled in the college, a type of high school in the city of Saintes where the principal, Abbé Louis-Augustin Hardy, was to exert great influence on the shaping of Gabriel's character through six hectic years.

Abbé Hardy was anything but impressed by his first experiences with Gabriel. The boy seemed not to care much for study. Instead, he seemed always to enjoy showing off the nuts and fruits which he brought to school each day.

When Gabriel had been at the college for a month, the abbé sent a report home to François. "A good father like you cannot feel very easy about a boy like your son," the abbé wrote. "He surpasses all the other students in sprightliness and light-mindedness. He is a very ordinary student. However, I hope time will make his fire subside."

In another report, written about three or four months later, the abbé told the father: "Your boy is about the same. He enjoys excellent health, and he is fat and happy. His progress is not apparent, but he is a good child."

Patience with the lively boy did bring some progress. By the end of Gabriel's first year at the college, Abbé Hardy was able to report: "He is less peculiar than he was in the beginning. He is a diligent student, and, if he does not lead his class, he is at least not at the bottom."

But there was little improvement in Gabriel's "light-mindedness." He was as mischievous as ever.

Gabriel was about thirteen years old and in his second year at the college when some stone masons were engaged to construct a new chapel for the school. One day he stopped below the scaffolding to look up at the workmen.

His dark, deep-set eyes were bright as he watched the workmen spread mortar so high above him. He had, like all boys, climbed many trees, but never had he been so high above ground as were these men. What might it be like, he wondered, to look down from such a high perch?

But no, he should not. The stone masons had warned him often enough as he had stood there looking up at them dreamily. Even in the classroom the good Abbé Hardy had charged the students to never, never attempt to climb the scaffolding. Not only was it dangerous, but such actions would only cause delay in completion of the chapel.

Gabriel looked up again. It would be wonderful to get so close to heaven! What harm could there be?

Impulsively he placed one foot on the lowest bar of the scaffold. His right hand reached out for a higher bar. His left foot soon joined the right and he was climbing up the wood struts.

"Fool! Get down!"

Gabriel heard the shout from above as one of the workmen spotted him. He pretended not to hear and continued his climb. Soon he was within five feet of the still-shouting workmen.

"Get down before you break your neck!" the workman shouted.

Gabriel finally looked up at the stone mason. The

man, cursing under his breath, waved at him to go back down. Gabriel took another step up.

The workman was holding a stone in his right hand. Now he swung his arm as if to throw the stone at Gabriel. Gabriel ducked his head to dodge the expected stone just as his right foot tried to locate the next rung on the scaffold. He lost his grip, and the ground, which was some twenty-five feet below, rushed up to meet Gabriel's fast-falling body.

A jagged scar across his jaw which was to remain throughout his lifetime was the only lasting result of his fall. Expulsion from the college was considered for a time, but Abbé Hardy interceded for Gabriel and he was allowed to remain. In the abbé's report to Gabriel's father, he wrote: "This accident may help him to overcome a defect which does not affect his heart."

The abbé was right. The accident certainly had an effect on Gabriel. His "light-mindedness" vanished overnight. The new Gabriel Richard was a seriously quiet and diligent boy, so much so that by the end of his second year Abbé Hardy could write: "He leads his class; he is full of good sense and emulation. He is a model for his fellow students. I deem you fortunate to have such a son."

Gabriel's last two years at the school in Saintes

"Fool! Get down before you break your neck!"

were without incident, except for continued progress in his studies. His great expectation was to go to the University of Paris, once he had graduated from the college, for study in philosophy and Greek.

Before he could enroll at the university, Gabriel's father suffered financial reverses that made it impossible to pay for university expenses. Gabriel seemed not to be bothered by the disappointment and began to consider more seriously the Abbé Hardy's suggestion that he would most likely find a rewarding vocation in the priesthood.

François Richard had hoped for law or medicine as the profession for his son and Gabriel, afraid his father might raise serious objections to his entering the priesthood, reminded his father that going to the Sulpician Seminary did not obligate him to the vocation. One or two years at the seminary would advance his education at little cost, and he might still return to either the medical or legal profession.

François gave in, and, after graduating from the college at Saintes with high honors, Gabriel Richard prepared to enter the Sulpician Seminary at Angers.

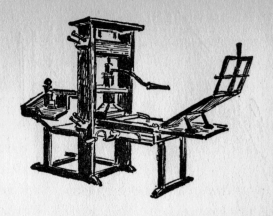

CHAPTER **3**

RUMBLINGS OF REVOLUTION

It is possible that, as he left his home for the Sulpician Seminary at Angers in October, 1784, Gabriel Richard had no serious intention of becoming a priest. If so, his mind had changed by the end of his first year in the Minor Seminary. But he did not tell his father.

That year was a pleasant one for Gabriel. The seminary was noted throughout France and Europe for the quality of priests it produced. Gabriel found

Gabriel let his father know of his decision.

great pleasure in discussing theological as well as civil matters with his classmates.

He took a full course of studies, happy that mathematics, which had not been taught at Saintes, was included. He could not have known it then, but his love for the science of mathematics was to prove most valuable in his later life.

By the end of his second year at the Minor Seminary, Gabriel felt he must let his father know of his decision to become a priest. Expecting strong resistance, he wrote: "I am always very docile to you, dearest Father. I respect and always will respect you.

However, I think it is my duty to request again your permission for me to take tonsure."

But there was no resistance or objection from François Richard. His reply told Gabriel: "I am not concerned with making you a priest, rather than a lawyer or physician, but only a good Christian and a faithful servant of God in whatever state you might be called."

Gabriel was relieved. The question was never again raised between him and his father, and, in 1786, he began his theological studies at the Major Seminary at Angers. Five years were to pass before he would be ordained.

His final year of study was at Issy, a suburb of Paris. Here, Gabriel was in the very shadow of the political center of France at the time when the rumblings of revolution were already being heard.

Not only in France, but also in many other parts of the world, men had risen and were rising in revolt against oppression. Liberal thinkers of the day, men like Thomas Paine and Thomas Jefferson of the new United States of America, John Locke of England, Rousseau and Voltaire of France, all wrote of a new freedom for mankind.

The dignity of the individual was the foundation

23

of this new freedom. Since any nation or State was composed of individuals, these *were* in truth the nation or the State. Therefore, these thinkers argued, should not the individual be *master* rather than the meek servant of a governor, king, emperor or president?

In France, the revolt against autocratic government began underground but quickly moved into the open. Anarchy, terror, and a bloody unending march to the guillotine followed.

The new leaders of France did not know where to draw the line. Institution after institution was forced to acknowledge the State as supreme. Then came a demand that the Church and all bishops and priests put God in second place. By January of 1791, every clergyman was to have taken an oath of allegiance to the State.

This order was condemned by the pope, and all French priests were forbidden to take the oath. One hundred and twenty-eight bishops and fifty thousand priests refused to take the oath while only four bishops and several priests weakened. Those who would not swear allegiance were called "nonjurors" and deprived of all rights. Many were arrested and imprisoned. Such bishops as were taken into custody were guillotined.

At Issy, Gabriel Richard—while not yet ordained a priest—held firm convictions on the matter. He was strongly in favor of the reforms and the principle of the dignity of man but could not accept the domination of the Church by the State.

Though he did not openly express his opinions, the mere fact that he believed as he did put Richard in the class of the nonjurors. At the time of the decree in 1791 the day of his ordination was nearing but, as a nonjuror, he might be denied ordination.

Ordination by a bishop who had taken the oath would be meaningless. This, Richard would not accept. A bishop who had not taken the oath could not administer the sacraments openly. Only in secret, therefore, could Gabriel Richard become the priest he so desperately wanted to be.

On October 9, 1791, Gabriel made his way unnoticed to a small house not far from the seminary. There, in a small room that had been converted into a chapel, young Richard was ordained by Monsignor de Bonal, bishop of Clermont, acting for the Bishop of Paris who was being too closely watched.

What should have been the happiest moment of Gabriel Richard's life was dampened by a feeling of hopelessness. He had dreamed of his ordination taking place in the Cathedral of Paris. Instead, it occurred in a small house with only a substitute bishop present. He had looked forward to returning to his home city of Saintes to say his first Mass in the church where he had worshiped as a boy, with his father, mother, sister, and brother and other relatives present. Instead, he offered his first Mass in Issy at the seminary's Shrine of Our Lady of Loreto.

Then, within two months of his ordination, the French government established the Committee of Surveillance to search for and arrest all priests who had not taken the oath. Day after day, Richard heard of friends or classmates who had been arrested.

Many of the Sulpicians had already suffered martyrdom. Gabriel Richard, as well as the others in the Order, would willingly have given their lives rather than compromise their beliefs. But living priests were needed to carry on the work, done surreptitiously or not.

The Superior General of the Society of St. Sulpice, Father Jacques Emery, earlier in the year had approached the Papal Nuncio in Paris with the thought of establishing a new headquarters in the United States. Archbishop Dugnani, the Nuncio, suggested it might be preferable to send a group of Sulpicians to establish a new seminary in Baltimore, Maryland, which had recently been designated as the first diocese in the United States.

Father Emery sent a representative to take up the matter with John Carroll, first Bishop of Baltimore, who was then in London. Bishop Carroll accepted the offer eagerly. Arrangements were made quickly to send four priests, the first group of Sulpicians to leave France for America.

Included in this first group of four was Father Michael Levadoux for whom Richard had a great affection. Gabriel was heartbroken at the departure of his good friend, little realizing that he would soon follow.

The day after Easter, 1792, the second group—Fathers Ambrose Maréchal, François Ciquard, François Matignon and Gabriel Richard—sailed from Honfleur in the dead of night aboard the brigantine *La Reine des Coeurs*.

As Gabriel stood on the deck of the brigantine and saw his beloved France slip away from sight, a great depression possessed him. He realized most keenly now that he had had no opportunity to say good-bye to his mother and father whom he had not seen for two years and—as fate was to decide—he would never see again.

Gabriel lifted his eyes from the water and looked up at the dark sky through eyes dimmed with tears. His lips formed a silent prayer that God would protect his father and mother and bring him home again while they still lived.

But, though Richard was depressed, he was not embittered. After all, he was doing God's will. He was going to a new land to serve the God he had vowed to serve throughout his life. He was going to a new land where there was freedom of thought and freedom to love that God as he chose to love Him.

CHAPTER 4

DISILLUSION

The morning of June 18, 1792, Father Gabriel Richard and his three priest companions were standing on the deck of the brigantine. It was Father Matignon who first saw the sketchy, irregular mass jutting out of the water on the horizon. Matignon pointed toward the west.

"Could that be America?" he asked in French.

Richard's heart seemed to leap within him. Perhaps

29

the long, hard trip was near an end. He turned toward the tall, heavy man coming toward them.

"*Mon capitaine*," Richard called out to the captain of the *La Reine de Coeurs*, "are we near America? Will we soon arrive?"

"It is the place in America called New Jersey," the captain replied. "We will turn south along this coast

The slow-moving brigantine sailed through
Chesapeake Bay.

to the Bay of Chesapeake and to Baltimore. It will be three, four, six days, as God and the winds will it. Who knows?"

It was actually six days before the slow-moving brigantine concluded its sail through Chesapeake Bay and docked at Baltimore. On Sunday, June 24, Fathers Richard, Matignon, Maréchal and Ciquard set foot on American soil.

The New World into which the four priests came was truly that. George Washington was President of the thirteen colonies which had banded together under the name United States of America. The constitution of this new land was only five years old, and in the ten years since the Revolution little land had been added beyond the boundaries of those first thirteen colonies.

The four priests reported to the small house which served as the bishop's residence. Father Richard, though wearied from the long trip across the Atlantic, anxiously looked forward to his new assignment. He was sure he would become professor of mathematics at either the new St. Mary's Seminary staffed by the Sulpicians or at Georgetown Academy which had been organized to augment the work done at St. Mary's.

There was another reason why Richard anxiously awaited his first visit to the seminary. His close friend Father Levadoux was working there.

Bishop Carroll rose from his chair as the four were ushered into the room and came to meet them. Each priest in turn—first Maréchal, as the senior of the group, then Ciquard, Matignon and Richard—knelt and kissed the bishop's ring.

The bishop asked about their trip, their hardships, their danger in fleeing France. He wanted to know all they could tell him about the conditions in France, and whether there was any easing of the persecution of the clergy. It seemed as though His Grace would never get around to telling them what their assignments would be.

It was Father Maréchal who finally broached the subject.

"We are most happy to be here, your Grace," Maréchal said. "We are at your service, ready to teach as you direct us at St. Mary's or the new academy."

A cloud seemed to darken Bishop Carroll's smiling face. He did not speak for a moment. When he did, it was in a low voice, tinged with sadness and regret.

"Matters have not progressed as we had hoped," the Bishop said. "The academy was established so that early education could be given the young men who would later enter St. Mary's. But it has not developed so. Now the academy takes over the work of the seminary. Our seminarians go to the academy to teach and there are no students for St. Mary's. So there is no place for you at St. Mary's or at the academy."

Richard's heart dropped as the bishop spoke. For what purpose then had he come to America? Was it only to turn around and go back to the turmoil and tension of France? Or would he be assigned to other work in other strange lands?

Standing there, waiting for the bishop to say more, Richard's lips formed a silent prayer that he might remain in this land where freedom was guaranteed.

There was a long silence. Perhaps Maréchal, as spokesman for the priests, felt that it was not his place to give answer to the bishop. And perhaps Bishop Carroll, sensing the disappointment which must have been evident on all four faces, felt that embarrassment would be lessened should one of them speak first.

Finally, it was Father Maréchal who broke the silence. "Your Excellency, is there need for us here in America?"

"Need?" Bishop Carroll echoed. Now his voice was strong. "There is such great need. If you desire, I can find a dozen assignments for each of you and for dozens like you."

A priest becomes a priest because it is his desire to fill the need of God's children. Where there is work to do, there he will go. He may be unhappy at the choice of work or place, but, as a priest, he does not question.

Bishop Carroll's enthusiasm had no limits as he spoke to the four of the great need for missionaries in all sections of the new country. He told them of its western boundary, the great river called the Mississippi, and that on this great river three settlements had already been established but there was only one priest to minister to all three.

He spoke of a village called Detroit. Though small, it yet was the hub of a great area called the Northwest Territory. He explained that this Detroit and its surrounding villages were part of the United States but were still administered by the British. Soon, when controversy over the area was settled and jurisdiction would fall to him as bishop of the only diocese in the United States, it would be necessary to send missionaries to this section surrounded by five Great Lakes.

The bishop outlined the problems occasioned by the closeness of the Spanish territory known as Louisiana, by the hostility of the Indians, by the inability of red man and white man to live together in peace.

When assignments for the four priests were made —and it seemed difficult for the bishop to determine where the four were most needed—they were separated. Maréchal, as the eldest and most experienced, would remain in Baltimore as aide to Bishop Carroll. In time, though it was not then known, Maréchal would succeed Carroll as bishop and later become archbishop of an expanded Diocese of Baltimore.

The New England area, where Protestantism had

taken a foothold, had great need of Catholic missionaries. To serve this extensive section, Father Matignon would be headquartered in Boston. Father Ciquard would go to Maine and work with the Abnaki
Indians.

And Gabriel Richard? He would go to the Northwest Territory where there were many Indian tribes.
Bishop Carroll named some of them, all strange but
musical names to Richard. Wyandots, Winnebagos,
Miamis, Pottawatomies, Chippewas and Ottawas.
Richard would join the priest who was administering
the three settlements, Kaskaskia, Cahokia and Prairie
du Rocher, on the Mississippi River in the Illinois
country.

The four priests thanked Bishop Carroll and they
prepared to leave. Suddenly, Richard remembered his
friend Michael Levadoux. Certainly he could visit
him for a little time before beginning his journey to
the Illinois country. He turned to Bishop Carroll.

"Excellency," he said, "Father Michael Levadoux
who came with the first Sulpicians—is he teaching at
St. Mary's or the academy? He is a very good friend
whom I should like to see."

"Father Levadoux?" Bishop Carroll repeated the
name. "A brilliant man, Father Richard. A brilliant
and a strong man. A man of great energy and a fine

administrator. He was too valuable a man for teaching when his talents could do so much elsewhere. He is no longer in Baltimore, Father Richard."

Richard had experienced disappointment after disappointment, but this must have been one of the most crushing. Not to be able to see his dearest friend for even a moment when the prospect alone had helped ease the pain of other disappointments!

"Since Father Levadoux is your great friend," Bishop Carroll continued, "you are most fortunate, Father Richard. It is Father Levadoux with whom you will work in the Illinois country."

CHAPTER 5

DOWN THE OHIO

On September 30, barely three months after his arrival, Father Richard left Baltimore with two guides for the Illinois country and a reunion with his friend Father Michael Levadoux. By horse, and by horse and cart, the small group crossed the mountains to Pittsburgh. A flatboat would carry them down the Ohio River to its juncture with the Mississippi and then north on the "Father of Waters" to Richard's meeting with Levadoux at Kaskaskia.

Another disappointment awaited Richard in Pittsburgh. He was very impatient with any delay. Day followed day and they were still in the little town where the Allegheny and Monongahela rivers joined to form the Ohio, the river down which they would travel to the Illinois country.

When two days had passed and they were still in Pittsburgh, Richard chastised his French-speaking guide.

"What is this delay?" he demanded. "Why are we in this dirty village when there is work waiting for me? Come, let us leave."

"It is impossible, *mon Père*," the guide told him. "The rough waters would smash our boat against rocks. We must wait for favorable waters."

They waited a full month before the "favorable waters" made it possible for them to continue their journey. Then, with his guides, Richard boarded the small flatboat, and the trip down the Ohio River began.

As they pushed off from Pittsburgh and made their way up the river, a puzzled frown came to Richard's face. He looked into the sky, first straight ahead, then right and left, and finally behind.

"Jean! Jean!" he shouted to his guide. "Stop! It is the wrong direction in which we go!"

The guide laughed. *"Non, non, mon Père!"* he

38

called out jovially. "Of a truth we go in the wrong direction. But that is this crazy river. First to the northwest, then to the south-southwest. And then the west-northwest before it turns south by southwest."

"How many leagues does this river go in such a crazy fashion?"

A thousand miles by flatboat down the Ohio

"More than three hundred and thirty leagues, *mon Père*," the guide answered. "But here it is spoken of as miles of which there are three in each league. So it is one thousand miles we must travel."

"One thousand such miles!" Richard exclaimed. "Twice the length of the Seine. Is it the longest river in the United States?"

"*Non, mon Père*," Jean answered. "Both the great Mississippi and the Missouri are more than twice as long as this Ohio."

Richard shook his head in wonderment and left Jean to his work of guiding the little flatboat through the safest, rock-free channels of the river. High cliffs flanked the water on both sides, cliffs studded with dense forests, the leaves of the trees all red and gold, brown and purple, since it was late October and the first frost had not yet come.

Now and then Jean would shout back to Father Richard, pointing as he shouted. Once it would be to his right and he would explain that it was the territory called Ohio and already there was talk that it would be one of the newer states added to the thirteen original ones. Then he would point left and shout that the land beside the river was that of Virginia in which the great Washington was born and lived.

Much of the information Jean provided Father Richard already knew, but the guide seemed so proud of his knowledge that Gabriel showed surprise whenever possible. Under such circumstances the journey continued, with Jean piloting the small craft toward one or the other of the banks of the river whenever he felt it was not safe to travel in the dark.

The second morning, Richard noticed that the land to his right which Jean had explained was Ohio was now more hilly than mountainous. On the hills he could see sheep grazing and here and there an isolated log cabin. Further down the river they passed the battlemented structure of a fort which Jean explained was Fort Von Steuben, named for the German officer who had helped Washington win the war against the British.

They later passed Marietta, also on the Ohio side. It was the first settlement in the area and had been named for Marie Antoinette. About four days after their departure from Pittsburgh, nearing the village of Gallipolis, Ohio, Father Richard could give Jean information he did not know. The guide had told him of the new town settled by Frenchmen.

"Ah, yes," Richard said. "But did you know, Jean, that the Society of St. Sulpice considered this village for a new Sulpician seminary?"

By now, the mountains had faded into the distance behind them and only high hills on either side of the river provided a break in the rolling and fertile lands of Ohio and Kentucky. Each day Richard became more entranced with the beauty and the possibilities of this wonderful new land which was to be his home.

It was near mid-afternoon of the eighth day from Pittsburgh when, to the right, Richard could see, nestled at the foot of a range of hills, what seemed like another fort. He called the guide's attention to it.

"*Oui, mon Père*," Jean called out. "It is Fort Washington. A new fort. Three, maybe four, years old."

Richard nodded. "Then the settlement there must be Losantiville."

Jean laughed. "*Was* Losantiville, *mon Père Richard*," he corrected Gabriel. "Since last year—maybe the year before, I think—it has been called Cincinnati."

Darkness had been falling earlier and earlier as they had moved further into the month of November. They were some few miles west of Cincinnati when twilight came and Jean guided the flatboat toward the Kentucky shore.

"We will be more safe from Indians this side of the river, *mon Père*," he explained. "Besides, there is much game. Perhaps Jean can provide the good *Père Richard* with food suited to such a man of God."

The flatboat was moored in a tiny inlet. Jean, leaving Father Richard and the second guide to make camp, collect firewood, and start a campfire, took his flintlock and disappeared into the thicket. Before Gabriel had the fire blazing, Jean was back, waving two plump rabbits joyfully.

While Jean was skinning the rabbits, the second guide came and touched him lightly on the shoulder. Jean turned and listened as the guide said something Richard could not hear. Then Jean grabbed his musket and ran to a large-boled tree near the shore.

Now Gabriel could hear the lap-lap-lap of water roiled by a paddle. Peering out toward the water he could just make out the shape of a canoe gliding through the river. Two men were in the canoe, but who or what they might be could not be determined in the half-dark of early night. One thing, however, was obvious. Whoever was in the canoe must have spotted the smoke of their campfire. The course of the canoe was straight in the direction of their camp!

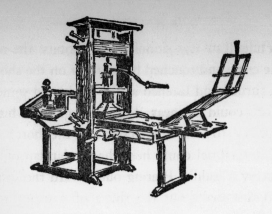

CHAPTER **6**

FATHER MICHAEL LEVADOUX

Jean, the guide, motioned to Father Richard to take cover behind a tree. The second guide did the same, and Jean remained in the shadows, his musket at the ready.

Soon the canoe hit the shore, and two men jumped to the dry land, one pulling the canoe to beach it on the bank. The other started forward, walking straight for the campfire.

As the man came closer to the light, Richard could see that he was dressed in black though the man's face was not identifiable.

"Hello!" the man called out. "Is no one here?"

Now the man turned so that his face was illumi-
nated by the fire.

Gabriel Richard gasped. He jumped from behind
the tree.

"Michael!" he shouted. "Michael Levadoux!"

Father Michael Levadoux stood fixed in his tracks,
his eyes straining to recognize the figure which had
called his name.

Richard came closer. "Michael, it is I!" he shouted
in French. "Gabriel. Gabriel Richard."

In a moment the two priests had embraced and were
pounding each other on the back. The two guides,
now joined by Father Levadoux's companion, also
obviously a Frenchman, stood by openmouthed.

"My friend. My good friend, Father Michael,"
Gabriel exclaimed. "But what are you doing in this
wilderness? You should be in Kaskaskia."

"Searching for you, *mon cher ami*," Father Levadoux said. "Bishop Carroll sent a message by courier
that you were coming as my aide. So I left Kaskaskia
hoping to meet you part way."

There was little sleep for either priest that night.
Father Levadoux insisted on hearing every detail of
the conditions in France and asked question after
question about his friends and classmates in the Society of St. Sulpice. Richard, on his part, had count-

less questions to ask of his friend about his time in Baltimore, about the parishes which they would together serve and about both the Indians and the French settlers who populated the Illinois country.

Levadoux smiled as Gabriel recounted what he knew about the Indian. Mostly they were fanciful reports he had heard from those who had never seen a red man.

"Ah, would that it were as you think, *mon ami*," Levadoux said sadly. "The Indian we see is not this noble nomad of the forests of which many have written. He is a barbarian. He is lazy. Oh, he is a creature of God and we must do for him as we would for any of our own countrymen. But he does not listen, and if he listens, he does not hear."

Gabriel listened, disillusionment growing in his heart every minute. "But you have converted many, many of them, Michael!"

Levadoux nodded. "Yes, that is true. But, my friend, what is conversion if there is no real faith? Most accept conversion only for the material good it may bring them. It means only that we work harder, hoping that one day understanding will come, that they will know God as we know Him."

When, finally, their conversation ended, and they stretched out on the cold ground, side by side, to get a

46

few hours' rest, Richard could not sleep. All he had heard from Levadoux bothered him greatly. Since his friend had said these things he knew they must be true. Yet they were almost unbelievable.

He had heard in Baltimore that the settlements along the Mississippi, the parishes he would help serve, were primarily French. That there the old French customs and the language had been preserved. That to be there would be little different from being in Marais, or Rochefort, or his home village of Saintes.

Yet the picture Father Levadoux had drawn of his parishioners was nothing like what he had expected. Michael had said that most seemed to have forgotten their lessons of faith, hope, and charity, took advantage of neighbor and Indian alike, and cheated either or both when they could get away with it.

Well, he decided, what needed to be done he would do. Michael had said that it meant only that he worked harder. He, too, would work that much harder. God had sent him to this place to help better the lot of His children. Whatever those children were, he, Gabriel Richard, would do what he could to better their lives. With this determination, Father Gabriel Richard finally fell asleep.

The following morning, sharing his friend's canoe,

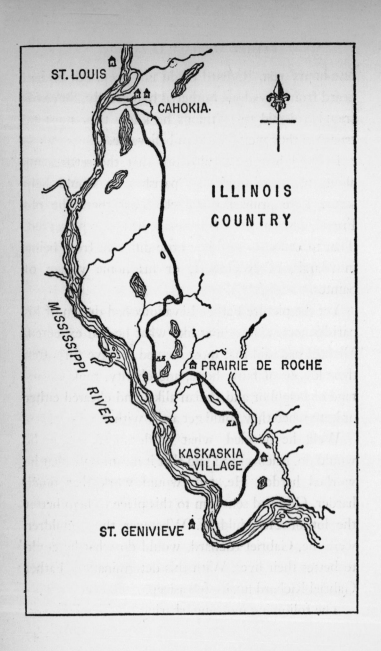

ST. LOUIS

CAHOKIA.

ILLINOIS COUNTRY

MISSISSIPPI RIVER

PRAIRIE DE ROCHE

KASKASKIA VILLAGE

ST. GENIVIEVE

he set off again down the Ohio. The trip to this point had been both tiresome and arduous. Now, it seemed travel was more dangerous, the river more treacherous. They lost much time skirting the falls in the river opposite the city of Louisville. Time and again they would hide in some inlet, camouflaged by dense foliage, until a marauding band of Indians passed.

It had taken a total of fourteen days to cover the full length of the Ohio River from Pittsburgh to its juncture with the Mississippi. Now, rowing north up the "Father of Waters" and against the current, it was to take them almost as long to travel the hundred and five miles to Kaskaskia as it had the thousand miles from Pittsburgh.

Twelve days after Richard sighted the Mississippi River for the first time, they set foot on dry land at Kaskaskia.

The first few weeks in Kaskaskia were interesting for Richard but not too eventful. He accompanied Father Levadoux on trips to the other two settlements. All three, Kaskaskia, Prairie du Rocher, and Cahokia, had been the sites of the earliest French emigrations to the area. They were already comparatively old and well established and would be the joint responsibility of the two priests.

Just a few hundred families made up the total white population of all three parishes and most of these were French Catholic. Richard, visiting one family after another with Levadoux, began to know most of them by name and to recognize their weaknesses as well as their needs.

Often, especially when he was in Cahokia, Richard would stand on the banks of the Mississippi and look across to the west. He could see there another settlement, much larger than Cahokia, Prairie du Rocher and Kaskaskia combined.

When he asked his friend about it, Levadoux answered that it was not American land but part of the Louisiana Territory controled by Spain. It was a great territory, Michael explained, stretching many miles southward to the great gulf near which was the important city of New Orleans.

"New Orleans?" Richard questioned. "But, *mon ami,* that is French, not Spanish."

Levadoux laughed. "So it is, Gabriel. And the city, like St. Louis, the settlement across the river from Cahokia, is more French than Spanish. Yet it is the Spanish who control it, as they control much of the land to the south of the United States. We have no jurisdiction there."

Each evening Richard and Levadoux would discuss the needs of their three little parishes and make plans to fill those needs. Then, each day, they would do what they could to make those plans come true.

It was in this manner that they built a church at Cahokia. With the help of a few laborers they constructed the church themselves. So strongly, so carefully was it built that the church still stands in Cahokia, almost two centuries later.

Richard worked hard and long without complaint, unless it was that there were too few hours in the day. With three widely separated parishes to serve—and only the two of them to cover the many miles—there was never time enough to accomplish all that either hoped to accomplish.

The inconvenience of constant travel forced Richard to move his headquarters to Prairie du Rocher in the summer of 1793. Levadoux remained in Kaskaskia. While there was still much going to and from the three villages, some time was saved. But, away from his friend, Richard became lonely.

To ease the pain of this loneliness he began to analyze what improvements he might make in himself to be of better service to God in his work in this strange country. One of his first realizations was that his English was pitifully weak. This he determined to correct.

With many English-speaking Catholic families near his home at Prairie du Rocher and a number of Protestants nearby—some of whom he felt sure would become converts—Richard did everything possible to improve his English. He wrote to Bishop Carroll asking for books that might help him learn. He asked the bishop to write his letters in English so that he might more quickly improve.

But progress was slow. Any time given to study could come only after all other duties were completed.

And Richard had many duties, many of which he imposed on himself. He found his own French parishioners badly in need of moral guidance and advice. They were a wild, careless lot. There was too much drunkenness and fighting among them. Too many were lazy. Not enough attended Mass regularly.

So Richard did not spare himself. After all, this was his first obligation. It was for this he was sent to the Illinois country. The welfare of his people, then, must come first.

Day after day, he drove himself to the point of exhaustion. To reach parishioners would call for paddling his own canoe or trudging through dense forests. In the winter months it was nearly impossible, with creek beds frozen over and the forests knee-deep in snow.

Through the years he spent in the Illinois country, Richard never complained outwardly. Now and then, as he thought of his parents whom he had left without so much as a good-bye, his loneliness would become unbearable. It was at such times as this that he drove himself even more desperately.

Four years passed during which Fathers Richard and Levadoux shared the work in the three settlements on the Mississippi with only an occasional passing missionary to help them. Richard's happiest and most satisfying moments during those four years were those he spent with Father Michael Levadoux. Their friendship was so close it seemed to make all the hardships worthwhile.

Then, near the end of the fourth year, even this pleasure was denied Richard. He was left alone as Father Levadoux was sent to the Michigan country.

CHAPTER **7**

STRANGE HAND OF FATE

The Michigan country was part of the huge Northwest Territory. It nestled between four of the five Great Lakes of the north. The French were the first white men to set eyes on this extensive, densely forested territory, Jean Nicolet having explored the northern shores of Lake Michigan as early as 1634.

The area stretched southward to the village of Detroit, established as a French colony in 1701 by Antoine de la Mothe Cadillac, then west to the town called "Chicagou" on the southwestern shore of Lake Michigan. The early French found all the Michigan area roamed by numerous Indian tribes. In the north and east were the Hurons, Ojibwas, Ottawas and Delawares. Shawnees, Pottawatamies and Miamis were in the south, fanning out from Detroit.

French relations with the Indians were friendly so there was little trouble in establishing two military and trading posts in addition to Detroit. These were Sault Ste. Marie and Michilimackinac in the far northeast of Michigan.

Sault Ste. Marie, located on both sides of the St. Mary's River, a stream which connects Lake Huron with Lake Superior, was the location of an Indian mission founded by Father Jacques Marquette in 1668. Michilimackinac, the name given to a large area at the northern tip of the lower Michigan peninsula which included Mackinac Island, had been discovered by Nicolet. A mission established by Father Marquette was also located there.

When the French and Indian wars ended with the surrender of the French to the English at Montreal in 1760, the British took over control of most of Michigan, including Detroit, as well as most of Canada.

With the coming of the English, the Michigan area became a hotbed of trouble. The Indians of the Michigan country got along well with the French. They hated the English who had made allies of the

Iroquois, despised by the Indian tribes in the North-west Territory.

In Michigan, the French had developed the fur trade into a great business. The trappers each season had tremendous catches, mostly of beaver. When the British took over Detroit in 1760, they found ware-houses filled with half a million dollars worth of furs.

The English wanted nothing to disturb this great trade. They passed laws making it unlawful to survey or acquire land in the Michigan territory either by patent or grant or by purchase from the Indians. Their hope was to discourage any permanent settlement in the area and so keep the fur trade steady through maintaining the wilderness and the forests.

The fur trade flourished in the wilderness

Then came the Revolutionary War. Though Michigan was far from the scene of action along the eastern seaboard, it was drawn into the battle on the side of the English. The British governor of the territory, Henry Hamilton, obtained permission to attack Americans in raids on the Ohio Valley and in western Pennsylvania.

Hamilton's forces consisted mostly of Indian warriors. He led them against American settlements on forays which were the chief disgrace of the war of the Revolution. Hamilton offered standing rewards for scalps, insisting that the Indians bring him only scalps, not prisoners, and so became known as "the hair buyer of Detroit."

After the American Revolution, the Treaty of Paris, signed in 1783, gave all the Northwest Territory to the United States. And this brought about the separation of Father Gabriel Richard and Father Michael Levadoux.

While the Territory was under the control of the British, all missionaries and priests who came into the area were under the jurisdiction of the bishop of Quebec. When control of the Territory passed to the United States, this jurisdiction was transferred to Bishop Carroll, as head of the only Catholic diocese in the new country.

But the change was not immediately made. The

British were slow in evacuating Detroit and Michigan, using every kind of excuse to delay their withdrawal. It took another treaty, one negotiated for the United States by John Jay in 1794, to exact a promise that the British would move out of the Northwest Territory by June 1, 1796. On July 11, the formal transfer of authority was made, and the "Stars and Stripes" flew for the first time over the garrison of Detroit.

Bishop Carroll realized the great need of the district for missionary help. Father Michael Levadoux was his choice, as might have been expected since the bishop had such great regard for Levadoux as a man and as an administrator.

Now Father Gabriel Richard was alone in the Illinois country.

And where two hard-working priests had shared the work of ministering to the three settlements on the Mississippi, now there was only one. Richard found it difficult enough being separated from his friend and left alone to cover such a vast territory, but his work was made even harder by the attitude of some of his parishioners.

First there was a minor dispute at Kaskaskia with Father Sièvre, a missionary who stopped in the area and gave Richard some help for a short while. Sièvre was dissatisfied with the way Richard scheduled the Masses which the two would say, and he made an issue of the matter. The parishioners sided with Sièvre, but Richard remained firm. It disturbed him that he had to report this dispute, which he considered a personal failure, to Bishop Carroll. But the bishop's reply was most understanding and helped restore Richard's confidence.

A short time later, while Richard was away from Cahokia for a few days, a more serious situation arose. While Richard was gone, Thomas Brady, one of his parishioners, decided he did not want to wait for the priest's return to get married. He arranged for a justice of the county, John Edgard, to conduct a civil marriage ceremony inside the church.

Richard returned to Cahokia on Saturday and was most disturbed. So upset was he over the irregular and un-Catholic actions of Brady in arranging for the civil marriage, and over the uncalled-for performance of the marriage by Edgard within the church, that he sharply criticized both Brady and Edgard from the pulpit the following day.

Brady was hurt. He made a special trip to Kaskaskia, the county seat, and gave Edgard an exaggerated account of Richard's criticism. Edgard and Richard had always been on friendly terms, but Edgard demanded that the priest appear before him to explain his remarks and apologize for them.

Richard did not think he had done anything wrong. In his mind only one thing was necessary to close the matter. Brady and his wife must be married in the church and by a priest in accordance with Catholic law.

But what to do about the judge's demand that he appear before him? Richard asked the advice of the parishioner with whom he boarded. The parishioner advised that he ignore the judge's request on the grounds that appearing to explain a church action would do harm to religion.

Richard and Edgard met accidentally on the streets of Kaskaskia. Since they had been friends there must have been some measure of embarrassment for both. Edgard was friendly, but cool, to Richard.

"Father," he told the priest, "I am not a Catholic so perhaps I do not understand your rules. But I cannot see the need for your demand that Brady be married again in the church. Certainly the marriage I performed is legal enough to satisfy the law."

"To satisfy the law, yes," Richard replied, "but not God, who has said that there must be a difference between a civil contract, such as your ceremony must

60

be considered, and an ecclesiastical contract which can be performed only by a representative of God."

Edgard shook his head. "You deal in fancy words, Father. I must deal only with facts. With law. And the law says that Brady is married. I must say that your conduct is contrary to law and, in view of that, I must so explain it to the Secretary of State of the United States."

Whether or not Edgard ever did write the Secretary of State is not known. At any rate, it seems that nothing officially was done. But rumors and counter-rumors spread over the entire area, and, for a time, Richard felt that his position was all but unendurable.

Again a kind, sympathetic reaction from Bishop Carroll gave him courage to go on. After a few months the entire episode seemed forgotten.

Though the unfortunate situation had left its mark on Richard's heart, he gave no indication of his hurt and buried himself in work. Letters from Michael Levadoux and from Bishop Carroll helped restore his spirits and brought with them hope for a change of assignment.

Levadoux had written about his own problems in the Michigan area. The three separated parishes in the

Illinois country had been difficult enough, but the Michigan territory was so much more extensive it was impossible to do it justice.

Not only was Levadoux pastor of St. Anne's in Detroit, but he had to oversee also such widely separated missions as those at River Raisin, about thirty-five miles south, Mackinac, about two hundred and seventy miles north, and Sault Ste. Marie, some seventy miles north of Mackinac.

Bishop Carroll had indicated in his letters what great importance he attached to the broad area being served by Father Levadoux, implying it might be necessary soon to send additional help to that territory.

Without Richard's knowledge, Father Levadoux had in various ways suggested to Bishop Carroll that he would welcome the arrival of Gabriel Richard. When the parishioners of the River Raisin mission prepared a petition to Bishop Carroll asking for another priest, Father Levadoux had gone so far as to include a postscript which said: "If you could only replace Fr. Richard so that he would be free to join me! I need his help badly."

The bishop was ready to reassign Richard but it was first necessary to find a replacement for the Illinois country. This was not easy. Finally, in early

1798, two young French priests, brothers, volunteered to go to Illinois, and Bishop Carroll notified Richard that he should go to Detroit to work with Michael Levadoux.

On March 21, 1798, happy and his heart filled with anticipation, Gabriel Richard left Illinois for Detroit. Rather than take the longer, but easier, route traveled two years before by his friend Levadoux, Richard, in his anxiety to get to Detroit, took what he considered a quicker way.

By canoe, Richard traveled down the Mississippi to the Ohio and east on the Ohio to its meeting with the Wabash River which formed what is now the southwestern boundary of the state of Indiana. Then he paddled his canoe some seventy-five miles up the Wabash to Vincennes, a full month having elapsed since he left Illinois.

The slowness of his travel is partly explained by his words in a letter from Vincennes to Bishop Carroll. "The Ohio was rising so much and the wind blew hard so often," he wrote, "that I could not go fast."

In that same letter he also told the bishop: "I will set out from this place immediately, and I hope to be at Detroit in at least a month." Either he miscalculated his travel time or, more likely, remained in Vincennes for a while to assist Father Rivet, assigned to

63

the Vincennes mission. Rivet had been ill for almost fifteen months, and Richard would hardly have left him after only a day or two.

At any rate, he did not enter the stockade at Detroit until June 3. Then, unexpectedly and unannounced, Richard surprised his friend Father Levadoux. Levadoux had been notified by Bishop Carroll that Richard should arrive sometime in mid-May and had become worried. But now that he saw his friend he embraced him warmly and welcomed Gabriel Richard to Detroit where, through his work during the next thirty-four years, he would leave his lasting mark.

CHAPTER **8**

DETROIT AND MACKINAC

Bishop Carroll had sent a third priest, Father Dilhet, to work with Fathers Levadoux and Richard. It was well that he did for two men could not have handled the assignment, so extensive was the territory under their charge.

The area was large and sprawling. On the one hand were the various tribes of Indians scattered throughout the territory and confining themselves to their own personal hunting grounds. On the other hand there were the white settlers, predominantly French, but with a generous sprinkling of British. These were concentrated in the settled sections of Detroit, River Raisin and Mackinac–Sault Ste. Marie.

Father Dilhet was assigned supervision of the little mission in the River Raisin district. All the territory north of the Raisin would be the responsibility of Fathers Richard and Levadoux. This included, in addition to far-off Mackinac and Sault Ste. Marie, a group of smaller communities north of Detroit along the Clinton, St. Clair and Black rivers, farming communities always considered part of Detroit.

Richard found that Levadoux had developed a great spirit of Americanism. In their conversations, the older priest would refer again and again to his admiration for the principles which brought about the United States. This sincere fervor of Father Levadoux soon rubbed off on Richard, and he, like his friend, became highly respected by the government authorities for his active patriotism.

The two priests divided their Detroit area obligations so that Levadoux, older and now in increasingly poor health, took care of St. Anne's inside the Detroit stockade. Occasionally, Richard would assist Levadoux at St. Anne's by performing the tasks of choirmaster or sacristan. Mostly he attended to the needs of the people in the French Catholic farming communities north of the village.

So it was for the first full year of Richard's stay in

The only priests in the sprawling northern territory

Detroit. During all that time, however, Father Levadoux kept hoping that his health might improve enough to enable him to send Richard to their northernmost missions, Mackinac and Sault Ste. Marie. Now he was able to do so.

On June 20, 1799, Richard boarded the *Detroit*, a government ship. Nine days later he sighted the fort at Mackinac on a cliff high above the straits which connected Lakes Michigan and Huron. The enthusiasm which greeted him on the island left a profound impression on Richard. So did the great amount of work he found had to be done.

There were about fifty families on the island and

almost all had children who had never been baptized. He had been there hardly two or three days when he reported in a letter to Bishop Carroll that he had administered the sacrament to more than thirty children who were over seven years of age.

The older people moved Richard to compassion. In his letter to the bishop, Richard said, "It is very sorrowful to see so many poor creatures quite abandoned without instructions." He was horrified that many did not know how to make the Sign of the Cross. He was further shocked when he heard that there were hundreds of others just as lacking in Catholic instruction throughout all the Northwest Territory.

Richard could not stand by under such circumstances. He immediately set about organizing classes for both adults and children, giving instruction in catechism and Catholic doctrine. The meetings were well attended, which pleased him considerably.

After two months in Mackinac, Father Richard paddled more than fifty miles across northern Lake Huron and into the channel connecting it with Lake Superior. Here he stopped for a short while at St. Joseph Island before continuing on to Sault Ste. Marie.

At the Sault, he was deeply shocked by conditions. Both white and Indian had little regard for decency, and drunkenness was common. Richard was so deeply concerned over the great need of the people in all the northern settlements that he was willing to remain there if Father Levadoux would give his permission.

Urged by many of the fur traders to stay, he wrote to Levadoux for permission. He sent his letter by an Indian courier named Oni-g-wi-gan.

Levadoux received the letter, but, his health again failing, he ordered Richard to return to Detroit immediately. Fearful that Richard, so sincere in his desire to bring God to the northern country, might write directly to the bishop, Levadoux himself wrote to Carroll, reminding him of Richard's importance to Detroit since the people there had great confidence in him and he could speak both French and English fluently.

Richard returned to Detroit on the British schooner *Charlotte*, arriving there on October 21 and praying that he might soon return to the Sault and to Mackinac. Not realizing Levadoux's dislike of losing him, he naively referred over and over again to the great need in the north.

"Michael," he would say, "you would cry tears should you see the people there and hear them plead. It is a bitter, cold country in the winter, I am told, but what is that when there is such great need."

Levadoux would shake his head sympathetically,

but he must have known in his heart that his own days in Detroit were numbered so he would say nothing. Then Richard, adding fuel to the fire of his argument, would say: "Ah, *mon ami*, it would be such a help to me in learning better English. There are few Roman Catholics amongst the English people here. It is different there and I would have so much more chance to practice my poor English."

Again, Levadoux would nod sympathetically and say nothing.

Through the following year and a half, Father Levadoux's health failed steadily. This meant an increase in Richard's responsibilities. In April of 1802, Father Levadoux was called back to Baltimore. He and Richard embraced in a warm farewell on the dock at Detroit, each assuring the other that they would again meet, and soon.

But their parting was a final one. After a year in the seminary at Baltimore, Levadoux was to return to France, a dream which would never come true for Gabriel Richard.

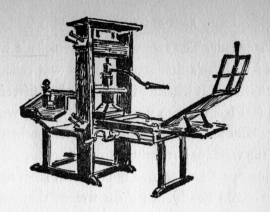

CHAPTER **9**

PASTOR OF ST. ANNE'S

As he signed the St. Anne's register as curé for the first time that May 3, 1802, Father Gabriel Richard was doubtful that he could administer his wide-spread parishes in the Michigan district alone. The responsibility of overseeing the spiritual welfare of such a vast area would weigh heavily on his thin shoulders until his death.

The Detroit in which he was headquartered was little more than a helter-skelter accumulation of wooden buildings within a twelve- to fourteen-foot-high stockade. The area within the stockade was the site of Cadillac's first settlement; it was called Fort Ponchartrain. It measured no more than fifteen hundred feet from east to west, paralleling the river, and only about four hundred feet from its southern edge near the water to its northern limits.

Four east-west and five north-south lanes or paths —you could hardly call them streets, they were so narrow—crisscrossed the interior of the stockade, with a gate at the eastern and western ends. A collection of military buildings—barracks, stables, and stores—faced an open square near the west gate. Just inside the east gate was Richard's St. Anne's church with its adjoining rectory and burial ground.

Both gates were closed tight and guarded from sunset to sunrise to safeguard citizens from hostile, drunken, or marauding Indians. But most of the citizens feared another danger far more than the wildest red man.

This was fire. The wooden buildings, clustered so closely within the stockade, were all so bone dry that the weakest spark could set off a holocaust.

Behind the stockade flowed the Savoyard River, little more than a small stream. Some three hundred or more feet beyond the Savoyard on a slight rise which gave a clear view of the Canadian shore on the opposite bank of the Detroit River, as well as a clear view of the river from north to south, stood the high ramparts of Fort Lernault. This had been built by the British when they controlled the area, deeming the stockade not practical enough for complete safety.

This, with the spread of small "ribbon farms" which stretched for miles from the eastern outskirts of the stockade, was the Detroit which first came to depend on the lean, gaunt priest clothed in a black soutane, his long, angular head topped by a shovel hat.

The doubts which first plagued Richard as St. Anne's new pastor faded as the civil authorities showed their pleasure at his kindliness and wisdom, and most of his parishioners gave him complete co-operation. Now and then those doubts would return, intensified, as others would criticize him for being too strict and challenge his authority.

One of the most disturbing rebellions within his parish came soon after Father Levadoux's departure. Richard had never believed in allowing young girls or women to act as "altar boys." He was aware that this practice, among others, had already been banned by Church decree and that Detroit, in common with so many frontier areas, had been merely slow in conforming.

73

When he tried to discontinue the girls' participation in ceremonial rites, the parents of some of the girls objected strongly. Some parishioners backed the parents. Others supported Richard.

Those who did not want to see the old practice stopped tried to force Richard's hand. They pushed the girls into going to the altar as services began. It became a dilemma for Richard who could not allow himself to continually interrupt a service when the result would be what he considered a sacrilegious argument in the church.

The matter came to a head at a Christmas service. Richard charged that one girl was indecently dressed and ordered her out. The entire congregation was in an uproar with group assailing group. The trustees of the church appealed to Richard to soften his stand, but the priest stood firm. He made it clear to the trustees that from that time on, as long as he remained the pastor, only men or boys would serve at ceremonies. The trustees, fearing they might lose Richard, supported his stand.

A period of peace followed during which Richard received some unexpected help. Father Dilhet had been having troubles of his own with the parishioners of the River Raisin settlement. These resulted in his

74

leaving the area and moving into St. Anne's rectory with Richard.

Richard was overjoyed, not only at getting the help he needed so badly, but also that it should be in the person of Dilhet whom he respected as a dedicated and scholarly priest. Now he would be better able to care for his obligations to the scattered missions immediately east and north of the stockade. And, even more important, he could give some consideration to the settlement at Mackinac.

He himself, three years before, had been the last priest to look in on the island to the north. Since that time, when Levadoux had refused his request to return, he had been worried about conditions in both Mackinac and Sault Ste. Marie.

Reports which had filtered back now and then showed the situation there to be intolerable. One trustee had died and the second had moved away so that there was no one to watch over the church and its vestments and sacred vessels. A dead dog had been placed on the church altar. The rectory was being used for any number of sacrilegious purposes.

Richard was grateful for Father Dilhet. Assigning him to the Mackinac area for six weeks saved the church there. Dilhet reorganized the parish, admin-

75

istered the sacraments of Baptism, Penance and Marriage. He also prepared a large class, including a number of Indians, to receive their First Communion.

When Dilhet returned to Detroit, Richard enlisted his help in a project which Father Levadoux had talked about with Richard but, with so much to be done, had never started. This was the badly needed reconditioning and enlargement of St. Anne's.

There was some talk of building an entirely new church of stone, perhaps outside the stockade. But no stone was available to them so this plan was discarded. The old St. Anne's would be rebuilt as much as possible, cleaned and renovated.

The project took two years. At the end, Richard and Dilhet could stand back and look at a church which was both more beautiful and more comfortable. Extra pews had been added, and a new roof installed as well as a steeple.

Richard and Dilhet were both proud of the finished church, even though the progress had been slow and all pledges to pay for the work had not been met. But the inconsistent parishioners took away what joy Richard had felt.

They criticized the way Richard had supervised the rebuilding and renovation, blamed him for the many delays and claimed that he meddled with the workmen. Richard, in his unhappiness at the seeming lack of appreciation of his parishioners, became depressed.

Now he felt tired. Now he began to dream of leaving Detroit, of returning to his home in Saintes, of again seeing his father and mother. He had done all he could for his people in Detroit. They had no need for him any more.

He wrote to Father Nagot, superior of the Society of St. Sulpice, about the possibilities of his being recalled to France. Father Nagot replied that it might be arranged in the near future.

He wrote to Bishop Carroll and advised him that he might soon be returning to France and a replacement for him should be found. And Richard even suggested to his trustees at St. Anne's that it would be well to be prepared to pay the transportation costs of his successor.

Fate was again to take a hand. When Richard began saying good-bye to his parishioners, those who knew the extent of his work and deemed him indispensable started a petition, and even got a court injunction forbidding his leaving Detroit.

Tuesday, June 11, 1805, a disaster wiped away any

desire Richard had for leaving.

The city on that day was preparing for a great, new change in its importance. Michigan had become, early that year, a Territory in itself, separated from the Indiana region with which it had been combined after the admission of Ohio to statehood in 1802. Now it was to have a territorial governor of its own and Detroit would be the seat of that governor.

It was a typical Tuesday in the farmers' market. The vegetables and fruits grown on the farms outside the stockade were being hawked, and, as sale followed sale, farmer and customer would talk about the new change for Detroit, or about the celebration being planned for the arrival of Governor Hull.

St. Anne's was crowded that Tuesday morning. Father Dilhet was saying Mass, assisted by Father Richard. Suddenly there was pandemonium.

Down in the western end of town, not far from the military barracks, was located the bakery of John Harvey. Either Harvey himself, or perhaps one of his employees, was in the adjoining stable smoking his pipe. A live coal fell from the pipe into a pile of straw, and in moments the stable and bakery were in wildly leaping flames that quickly spread to the buildings on both sides.

One bone-dry wood building after another caught fire as the flames were fanned across the narrow streets. The volunteer fire department was helpless, and citizens and soldiers from the fort pitched in valiantly trying to contain the spreading flames. People, driven from their homes, wildly made for the river and paddled canoes away from the shore to escape.

In the church as the cry of "Fire" went up, Father Dilhet tried to calm the worshipers who were streaming toward the doors, pleading with them to help one another. Father Richard gathered together the sacred vessels as Father Dilhet grabbed what vestments and books he could carry, then both made their way to a field outside the stockade.

Richard hesitated in the field only a minute to deposit the valuables he had saved. He rushed back into the town, salvaging what supplies he could, giving comfort to those who had lost their homes and arranging shelter for them.

Detroit was a mass of smouldering rubble. As the smoke cleared and the fire subsided, only two buildings could be seen still standing where three hundred had stood a few hours before.

Tears filled Richard's eyes as he located the spot where the steeple of the rebuilt St. Anne's should have been. But there was no despair evident on his face. A firm decison marked the thin line of his set lips.

As his eyes swept across the ruins, every thought of

Detroit burned like tinder.

leaving Detroit, of returning to France, faded from Richard's mind and heart. His people were in dire trouble. They needed him as they had never needed him before. He could not leave them. He would not leave them.

Those standing near heard him mutter a prayer of hope. They heard words which were to symbolize one day the spirit of a great city, words which were to become part of the seal of the city of Detroit.

"*Speramus meliora. Resurget cineribus.*"

"We hope for better things. It will rise from its ashes."

CHAPTER **10**

THE FORCE OF LOVE

It is possible that Gabriel Richard was not conscious of the great love he had developed for the new country in which he worked. Perhaps the fire and fervor which drove him had grown slowly, planted first by the earnestness of his friend Father Michael Levadoux.

At any rate, now in a time of common tragedy, Richard felt closer to all his people, whether or not they were French, whether or not they were Catholic. He felt an obligation to serve everybody and spent hours and days trying to restore the hopes of those who had lost everything in the disastrous fire.

Shelter was needed for those who had been burned out of their homes. He visited the farms and homes in the settlements outside the stockade as well as on the Canadian side of the river and asked for beds and living quarters for those who could be accommodated. He helped some families move into tents, provided by the military authorities and set up in the fields which surrounded the town.

All the stocks and provisions in Detroit had been burned, so food for the homeless was even more necessary than a place to sleep. He organized groups and led them in canoes and flat-bottom boats east and west on the river, begging the farmers for vegetables, milk, eggs, and other foods.

There were hardly enough hours in the day to accomplish a part of this. Yet he always found time to stop and try and erase the despair of those who were convinced there was nothing left for them in life. Many nights Richard went without sleep.

Detroit had no civil authority at the time since the new Territory would not be officially established until July 1, almost three weeks after the date of the fire.

83

Richard begged the farmers for food.

Not until then would Governor Hull arrive.

Who, then, could the people turn to except their priest, Father Gabriel Richard?

It was only natural that, as the people forgot their misery and misfortune, they should begin to think of rebuilding their homes. They began to make plans with Richard's help, but the shortage of lumber delayed any actual construction.

On June 30, Judge Augustus Woodward, newly appointed as chief justice of the Michigan Territory arrived in Detroit to join his associate justice, Frederick Bates. When Judge Woodward saw the extent of the devastation, he suggested that any building plans should wait until the new governor arrived.

Richard saw the wisdom and probable benefits to the people in the judge's suggestion. His people agreed to wait a few more days before going any further with rebuilding plans.

Governor Hull entered Detroit the following day, July 1, and swore in his two aides, Judges Woodward and Bates, in ceremonies in front of the open-air altar Richard was using to say Mass. This gesture on Hull's part gave the people, almost all of whom were Catholic, added confidence.

The governor's inaugural talk, given in English but translated into French by Richard, promised the citizens that there would be no delay in rebuilding the village. But, he told them, he agreed with Judge Woodward's idea of first setting up a master plan for enlarging the town and beautifying it through larger lots and wider streets.

Judge Woodward, who had spent many months in Washington, had always considered the plan for the capital city as drawn up by the French army engineer and architect, Pierre Charles L'Enfant, to be ideal. For Detroit, Judge Woodward suggested a similar layout with wide avenues and streets, and many circles and parks. The new Detroit, as conceived by Judges Woodward and Bates and Governor Hull, would include, in addition to the original village, much of the government-owned fields which surrounded the stockade. It was proposed, under this plan, that exchange would be made of land plots inside the old section for other plots, larger and more suitable for residences. For this, however, they would have to wait for the federal government to approve transfer of the land to the city.

Most of the citizens were willing to wait since the prospect of a larger, more beautiful town was so appealing. But others were impatient and began to build on their original property.

Two years were to pass before Congress would authorize the property exchange. Naturally, the long delay caused the citizens considerable hardship. This led to great resentment directed especially at Governor Hull. The governor was not a strong personality. He was weak and timid, and he was a poor administrator.

Where Governor Hull was weak, Judge Woodward proved to be strong. He was a man who put the interests of the people before his own and this endeared him to Father Richard. The two became close friends. It was this friendship which helped ease the pain of the two-year delay and saved the planning of the new city from complete chaos.

When Congress finally gave approval for exchanging land within the old town for plots of ground on the commons outside the stockade, rebuilding plans moved quickly. Richard, naturally, was overly anxious to get his new church constructed. Immediately after the fire, he had constructed his open-air altar which served him well as long as the weather remained mild. When fall brought a radical drop in temperature, he rented one of the two buildings which had escaped the flames.

But three years in the building—it was an old

87

warehouse stocked with smelly furs—were more than enough. Richard looked forward to the new church built on a new site offered to the parish by the two judges and the governor.

The location of the land which was offered appealed greatly to Richard, as it did to some of his parishioners. It was in an area which he felt sure would increase in value considerably once the rebuilt city began to approach its potential. Too many of the parishioners were not that enthusiastic. They fought the exchange and all but succeeded in defeating it.

Judge Woodward's street layout for the rebuilt city called for an important east-west avenue named for President Thomas Jefferson to cut directly through the cemetery on the old church property. Richard had already planned on a new burial ground north of the stockade and was ready to supervise removal of the bodies from the old churchyard.

The parishioners who opposed the exchange came up with excuse after excuse. They brought up old superstitions about the disturbance of the dead. They thought up plan after plan to block acceptance of the new land.

A committee was formed. Petitions were signed. The matter was taken up before Governor Hull and

Judges Woodward and Bates. What should have remained a church disagreement mushroomed into a
political argument.

When the opposition's legal efforts to block removal of the graves failed, Richard began evacuation
of the cemetery ground. But, as the ground was dug
up over old graves, the objectors milled about and
shoveled as much dirt back into the graves as was
being shoveled out.

Richard felt certain the opposition had not given
the true reasons for their objections. The real motive,
he believed, was to force him to locate the new
church closer to their homes. Most of the objectors
came from the same northeastern area. For the sake of
peace, and hoping to stop any split in his congregation, Richard held up the removal of the bodies from
the cemetery.

The objectors were not appeased. They were part
of a group which had, immediately after the fire and
without consulting either Father Richard or the trustees of St. Anne's, bought land and an old building on
the northeast shore of the river, intending to convert
the building into a church.

Now, with the dispute raging over the location of
the new church, the group renewed its efforts to have

the new St. Anne's built on their land. They got nowhere with their arguments and sat back, doing nothing, expecting that Richard would ultimately be
forced to come to them. They refused to make any
contributions to St. Anne's.

As time went on and a building on the grounds was
converted into a chapel, Father Richard did say Mass
there occasionally. This, he felt, was his duty; it did
not indicate a change of his mind.

It took ten years before the trustees of St. Anne's
finally agreed to accept the land which had been originally offered. An extra plot was added to the original, and in 1816 the transfer was made.

But there was still opposition to the building of the
church on the land. Two more years had to pass before Richard could go ahead with his new church.

While the battle of the church site had been raging
in Detroit, changes had taken place in the hierarchy
of the Catholic Church in America. Bishop Carroll
had long realized that the United States was growing
much too fast and its frontiers were being pushed
too far away from the eastern seaboard to be administered by a single diocese. Acting on his recom-
mendation, Rome created four new dioceses. Three
sees were to be located in the east, at Philadelphia,

Boston and New York. The fourth, which included Michigan, would be at Bardstown, Kentucky.

Benedict Joseph Flaget, a Sulpician priest and old colleague of Gabriel Richard's, was named Bishop of the Bardstown diocese and so became Richard's superior. Bishop Flaget took it upon himself to make the decision as to where St. Anne's would be located.

He came to Detroit in 1818 and brought the disagreeing factions together. Then he announced that the new St. Anne's would be built on the plot of land offered by the government and accepted by the trustees of the church two years before.

The controversy was ended. Richard was upheld. He could now go ahead with his plans to build a new church.

CHAPTER **11**

ALL ARE GOD'S CHILDREN

While the controversy raged over the location of the new St. Anne's, Father Richard found it necessary to look about for another temporary church. The warehouse in which he had been holding services was no longer either adequate or desirable.

Then, too, after the fire had destroyed his church and rectory, Richard had lived as a boarder with whichever parishioner could take him in. This was also no longer practical.

Down the river and west of the stockade, he located some property known as Spring Hill Farm. The previous owner had lost the farm through nonpayment, and it had been taken over by the federal government.

The moment he saw the well-equipped buildings on the land, Richard felt that here was an opportunity to accomplish a double good. He leased the farm and the buildings from the government for $205 a year and moved his headquarters to Spring Hill. It was the year 1808.

In leasing this land he had no intention of giving up the fight for a new St. Anne's on the site which had caused such a commotion. No, he saw it as the possible answer to a dream he had cherished since coming to the Michigan country.

He would have a church or a chapel at Spring Hill and also a school devoted to the vocational training of Indians. An area on the river near Spring Hill had been a centuries-old gathering place for Indians. Indians still used it as a meeting place. It would be ideal for his missionary and educational work.

But a dream such as Richard had for Spring Hill Farm takes money. Richard had too little with which to carry on his work. The difficulties in the parish,

93

with so many of the parishioners refusing to make any contributions, had drained any extra money he might have used.

Richard discussed his hopes for Spring Hill with Judge Woodward. The public-spirited judge saw the value to Detroit and the country in Richard's plan. He suggested that Richard go to Washington and appeal directly to the President and to Congress.

Judge Woodward gave him personal letters of introduction to President Jefferson as well as influential congressmen and senators, and Richard left for Washington. He arrived there in January, 1809, and was warmly received by the President. Jefferson was very much impressed by the thin, ascetic-looking priest's dedication and enthusiasm.

Richard felt very much encouraged as he left the President's office. For a while he had thought he might be asking too much to request not only that Spring Hill Farm be given him outright but also that the government give him an appropriation to assure the education of Indian children.

He faced congressional appointments the next day with calm assurance, speaking to each legislator with confidence. "Everybody knows," he said, "that Indians will do nothing to feed or clothe their children at the schools. Therefore, if the government wishes to have them civilized, and make them useful members of society . . . it becomes now a duty on the part of the American white people to come to the assistance of their red brothers."

He spoke at length about the conditions under which the Indian lived, of his natural indolence and distrust of the white man. He pointed out that if Congress would only help the Indian to help himself it could well prevent a war which might destroy the Michigan settlements.

He told the congressmen, as he had told the President, that he had been empowered by the Wyandot tribe to speak for them. And for the Wyandots he had a plan, he explained. He asked if Congress would authorize the granting of a farm allotment to the head of each family of the tribe, and to each youth of the tribe who would receive eight years of education at Spring Hill. The land allotments would be cut from acreage between the Huron and Ecorse rivers, land that was then occupied by the Wyandots. Land not alloted, he said, could be kept in reserve and used as inducements for Indian children who made extraordinary progress at the school.

The sympathetic understanding of the President and the kindly attention with which the legislators listened made Richard certain he would get the help he requested. He left Washington for visits to New York and other eastern cities in such high spirits that he selected an organ, a harpsichord and a printing press and had them shipped back to Detroit. Each was the first of its kind to be seen in the Michigan Territory.

After his return to Detroit and while waiting for the word to come from Washington that his requests had been approved, Richard began planning for the future. So sure was he that Congress would give him title to Spring Hill Farm that he did not pay rent for the property in 1809. This proved to be a serious mistake.

Richard's request had, in fact, been placed before Congress and referred to the House of Representatives' Committee on Public Lands. But there were other and, to the members of the committee, more important matters to consider.

Meanwhile, local citizens who had their eye on the property used the failure of Richard to pay the rent as a lever to induce the government to offer the property for sale at private auction. Richard could raise nowhere near the five thousand dollars for which the property was sold. His dreams for Spring Hill collapsed.

Even though his dream was shattered, his hopes

remained at high pitch. He merely began again and searched for another location. Not far from Spring Hill he found another farm which he made do. Here, in an old barn which he fixed up into a church, rectory and school combined, he began to help the Indian raise the level of his living.

His congregation at St. Anne's had fought with Richard over the location of the new church and his hopes and dreams for Spring Hill had been shattered by the avarice of men to whom money and power were everything, but Father Gabriel Richard took his troubles and disappointments in stride. There was too much to do, too many whites as well as Indians who needed his help, for him to waste time and energy in either self-recrimination or question of why his efforts did not meet with immediate success.

And it was not only his Catholic brothers who could call on him. Since there was no Protestant minister in the Detroit area, and for more than ten years no other clergyman of any denomination in the district, he turned away no one who needed his sympathetic understanding. And he did even more.

Because he respected and was respected by the English-speaking Protestants in the village, he made himself available to them in one of the earliest examples of true ecumenical spirit on record.

97

The territorial government had built a Council House, a sort of government building where Indian councils might also meet. The Protestants of Detroit invited Richard to conduct services for them on Sunday afternoons. They might willingly have come to his church but, rather than embarrass them, Richard suggested that the services be held in the Council House.

There, every Sunday, in addition to his own services at St. Anne's, Father Richard conducted nondenominational services which are more correctly described as a series of discourses and discussions on basic religion. As might be expected, Catholics in the area were disturbed by his actions. They believed that a Catholic priest should preach only to Catholics and only about Catholic doctrine.

Richard's dedication to his work as a man of God could not let him accept this narrowed view of a priest's responsibilities, but he was, regardless, disturbed by the commotion his activities caused. He felt in duty bound to explain his feelings to Bishop Carroll.

"This letter is to have you advise me on a point of my present conduct that seems somewhat irregular on some respect," he wrote the bishop in a letter dated

1807. He went on to explain how and why he had begun his service to the Protestant group, explaining that "in the whole town there are no more than two English persons of the Roman Catholic Society." He ended his letter asking the bishop's direction "on this important affair."

The bishop must have agreed with Richard's work and given it his blessing for Richard continued to meet with his Protestant friends until 1831.

For his own countrymen, the French people of the area, Richard was always concerned. As time went on, this concern deepened. Even after the establishment of the territorial government, the French continued to group together. They did not familiarize themselves with the American customs which became more and more the customs of the area. Few of them could even write their own names in English, much less read, and there was little chance that their children would be any more literate than they. Richard foresaw trouble ahead for his people if they did not know and respect the laws of the Territory.

Richard did what he could to impress on the French the need for educating their children in the English language and the importance of familiarizing themselves with American laws and customs. To help

99

them, Richard assisted in the preparation of a petition to Congress requesting that the territorial laws be printed and published in French. This was done.

Just as for his own people, there was never too much Richard could do for the Indian. He was especially disturbed over the government's claiming Indian lands without fair payment. He had been witness to a number of situations and realized that many mistakes were being made to the detriment of the red man. He did not believe that the government intended to cheat the Indian and felt that if the authorities only knew the errors being made and the dire results that might follow, the situation might be improved.

He could not bring himself to interfere directly, but he did write his views in a letter to Bishop Carroll, outlining all the errors he thought were being made in dealings with the Indians. Carroll was so impressed with the letter and its sincerity that he forwarded it to the Secretary of War. The Secretary, in turn, made certain that it was read by the President. Quickly, new instructions for the purchase of Indian lands were drawn up. A more clearly defined Indian policy was created.

Richard's concern for the Indian went far deeper. He was most distressed for the little Indian children who came to him for instruction. They had little to wear, being, as he wrote, "almost naked, dirt and worms excepted."

With President Jefferson and congressional leaders in Washington, and with Governor Hull and the justices in Detroit, he always turned the conversation around to the most important need of the Indian, education. If and when there would be money provided for schooling the Indians as he thought they should be schooled, he intended putting emphasis on vocational courses.

Let the Indian children, he said, "make their own bread, grow hemp and flax, let them make their own clothes, let them learn to build their own houses, let them take care of the sheep which will supply the wool to clothe them. Let the girls spin that wool, and move the shuttle, let them milk the cows, and raise large quantity of chicken."

He believed, too, in giving them incentive to do these things. He suggested that when the schools were established provision should be made to reward the best students. So that they might have pride in their accomplishments the children should be given their awards in public ceremony to the sound of band music. "Such public exhibitions," he insisted, "should certainly excite the ambition of the children and draw the attention of their parents."

In their own way, the Indians loved Richard and had great confidence in him. Their chiefs held him in high respect, begging him to send missionaries to teach them.

On one such occasion, Pokagon, chief of the Pottawatamies, came to ask that Richard send a priest to his tribe. There was none available and Richard himself could not leave Detroit. Pokagon misunderstood the reason why his tribe could not have a missionary. He dropped to his knees at Richard's feet and recited the Ten Commandments, the Apostle's Creed, the Hail Mary, and the Lord's Prayer.

"See," he said looking up at Richard. "Pokagon is good Christian."

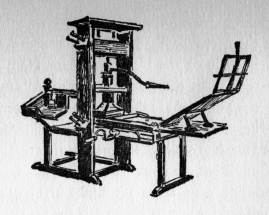

CHAPTER **12**

RICHARD'S PRINTING PRESS

When Gabriel Richard left Washington after what he believed to be a very successful meeting with President Jefferson and congressional leaders, he went to New York in the hopes of getting financial support from some of the prominent Catholics in the state. He had moderate success in New York City and went northward to Albany. Somewhere along the way he acquired the organ and harpsichord which he had shipped to Detroit.

Leaving Albany he began his trip back to Detroit

along the Mohawk Trail which paralleled the Mohawk River in central New York State. He traveled
some fifty miles the first day out of Albany and
stopped for the night in the village of Herkimer. The
following morning, before he resumed his journey, he
entered the shop of G. G. Phinney, a printer.

Before he left the shop, Richard had purchased an
old printing press and some banks of type which
Phinney had for sale. What he paid for the press and
type or what he may have used for money is not
known. But the printing press was purchased and sent
on its way to Detroit.

Richard had delayed so long in Herkimer, no
doubt bargaining with Phinney, that he covered
hardly ten miles that day and stopped for the night in
Utica. In the few waking hours he spent in this town,
he met James Miller, printer by trade. How he per-
suaded Miller to leave Utica and go to Detroit to
operate the printing press is a mystery. But this he
did. It is also very likely that Miller went first to
Herkimer and perhaps helped crate the press and
type. Miller, the press, and a supply of paper arrived
in Detroit about the same time.

Richard had for many years hoped for a printing
press. Detroit had none and he felt keenly the need of
at least something which might pass for a newspaper.

Only an informed citizen could be a good citizen, Richard believed. To fill the gap, before his purchase of the printing press, his sexton would stand on the steps of St. Anne's church after Sunday mass and cry out the news.

Births, deaths, new laws, political news, all were announced to the parishioners who stood around and listened avidly. Often the news crier would include items of special interest to the people, such as sales of yard goods at local stores, land available for purchase, auctions of cattle or horses, and even the times and places of picnics or horse races.

Richard reached Detroit about mid-July. On August 31, The Michigan *Essay*, or *Impartial Observer*, made its first appearance on Detroit streets. It was the village's first home-printed newspaper.

The Michigan *Essay* was a very small paper by today's standards. It consisted of only four pages, nine and one-fourth inches by sixteen inches. News carried on the four-column pages included "foreign" items taken from Liverpool, London, and Paris journals and "national" news from Boston, New York and Pittsburgh papers. Most such news was, of course, from two to five months old by the time it was reprinted in the *Essay*.

Few of the French people in Detroit could read

English, so Richard prepared a column, sometimes two, in French for each issue. The balance of the paper was all English, edited by James Miller who also served as publisher.

This weekly newspaper was only one product of the Richard Press, as the business came to be known. This was fortunate. The newspaper failed through lack of advertising revenue and poor circulation. Some few copies of the first issue are still preserved. But there is no way of knowing how many editions other than the first were ever printed. None beyond that first have ever been located.

Though the newspaper failed, the Richard Press was a complete success. There was a vital need in the town for the printing of business forms and pamphlets. Government documents and legal notices were printed at the Press. Then came an outpouring of books of which there were so few in any frontier town.

The first book to be printed by the Richard Press must have been published within two weeks or so of Richard's return. This was *The Child's Spelling Book* which bears an August 1, 1809 date. Richard was thrilled at the prospect of bringing information as well as pleasure to his people.

The paper failed, but the press thrived.

As might be expected, since he was a dedicated and devoted priest, much of the printed material was religious in nature, prayers and prayer books, missals, the majority of which—since they were intended mostly for his congregation—were in French. In 1810, a book titled *The True Principles of a Catholic* was published.

General educational books were not slighted. Richard, with a firm belief that only knowledge would bring real understanding to his people, kept a stream of schoolbooks, histories, and reprints of the classics rolling from his Press.

This simple printing press which Richard picked up in Herkimer, New York, did far more than entertain and enlighten the people of Detroit. It also had a profound effect on the political life of the entire Michigan Territory.

Richard, himself, was most interested in political affairs. A public official, in his mind, was the servant of the people. The people, therefore, should know not only what their officials did but also the future significance of what was being done. Richard used his Press to report on important civic activities even after the failure of the Michigan *Essay*.

Off the Richard Press on September 26, 1809,

came a handbill containing the full report of a grand jury decision severely criticizing Governor Hull. The handbill listed the examples of official misconduct and abuse of power with which the grand jury charged the governor. Within a month later, the Richard Press printed a second handbill in French, a reply by Governor Hull defending himself against the charges.

The two handbills which, between them, gave both sides of the controversy, were very likely responsible for the meeting of a committee of citizens in October of that year. This meeting adopted a resolution asking Congress to abolish the governor and judges system of management and replace it with a form of elective representative government.

The resolution voted on by the citizens at that meeting was printed in both French and English by the Richard Press. Copies were sent throughout the Michigan Territory as well as to members of both houses of Congress in Washington.

The beautifully bound, 138-page book published in 1816 comprising all the acts and laws of the Territory of Michigan was perhaps the last to be produced by the Richard Press. Titled *Cass Code*, it may well be the most lastingly useful. Named for Lewis Cass who had succeeded Hull as territorial governor in 1813, this book served for years to come as the reference on which all Michigan laws were based.

The purchase of his printing press may have been a whim of the moment as Richard paused in Herkimer, New York. It may have been the dream of years. There is no way of knowing which, if either, it might have been.

But, whim or dream, it did great service in every phase of Detroit and Michigan life. Of that there is no doubt.

CHAPTER **13**

WAR AND ANOTHER DISASTER

Everyone familiar with the British realized from the day they were forced out of Detroit and the Michigan Territory that they would plan to retake the Territory one day. It took sixteen years before it finally happened.

Through all of those sixteen years, Detroit, with only a mile of river separating it from the British garrison in Canada, was in constant fear of attack. This was fear not only of the British themselves but, even more so, of Indian massacre.

Richard had done his best to see that relations between the Indians and Americans were friendly. The red man had always been so with the French who were reasonably fair in their dealings with the natives. But the short sightedness of some of the congressional leaders in Washington and the greediness of some Americans along the frontier combined to increase the distrust of the Indian for the white man in the States.

The English lost no time in taking advantage of this distrust. They influenced tribes in Ontario. They sent agents to tribal meetings below the border. In every case they reminded the Indian chiefs of the broken American promises and of the tribal hunting grounds taken from them for small or no payment at all.

This resulted in a number of Indian raids on American settlements even before the outbreak of actual war. Scalping raids and kidnapping parties became the terror of the small settlements in the wilderness. The settlers, in revenge, would lie in wait and attack innocent Indian hunting groups. It was a vicious, bloody cycle.

Even though all indications pointed to an open outbreak at any time there was little protection for the frontier outposts of the Northwest Territory when war finally broke out in the summer of 1812. The British found little resistance in retaking most of the territory from northern Illinois east to Ohio.

Military preparations for protection of the border were not made until war had broken out. A brigade of not-too-well-trained Ohio militiamen was sent to Detroit along with a regiment of regular army to augment the local militia. The entire force, totalling less than three thousand men, was to be commanded by Governor Hull.

In organizing the Detroit militia there was considerable sentiment that the French citizens of the area should not be included. Rumors had spread that because of their friendliness to the Indians and their seeming preference for the English they were not to be trusted.

Gabriel Richard, French himself but intensely loyal to the United States, had done his work with his people well. A good percentage of the local militia as it was finally organized were French. There was never a doubt of their loyalty, and all proved to be good fighting men though they had little chance to show their worth.

In July of 1812, General Hull led his troops into Canada. His only opposition was a much inferior British force. With everything in his favor, Hull would not give the order to attack. He delayed for days, giving the British an opportunity to bring up reinforcements.

There is no definitely known reason for Hull's delay in attacking. It is believed that soon after crossing the river into Canada he heard that Fort Dearborn, at Chicago, had been captured and everybody massacred, and that later he learned that Mackinac also had been taken and the warlike Chippewa tribe was on its way to join the American-hating Shawnees, Wyandot, and Pottawatami tribes being led by Chief Tecumseh and moving on Detroit. Hull, terrified by the thought of thousands of savages joining the British in battle against him and his army, ordered a retreat back to Fort Lernault beyond the Detroit stockade.

On August 16, 1812—less than two months after the start of the war—Hull, suddenly and without a shot having been fired, surrendered his entire army to the English general, Sir Isaac Brock. Brock was a fighting man. He turned over command of the Michigan Territory to the senior officer of his staff, Colonel Henry Procter, and left for other battlefields.

Procter was hard, harsh, and brutal. Though they were helpless, the citizens of Detroit were enemies in his eyes and to be treated as enemies. He initiated restrictions, set up rules of conduct, and made de-

114

mands on the people that had them all but strait-jacketed. But he neither controlled nor bothered the Indians.

No person and no piece of property was safe from assault or plunder. Everyone in Detroit lived from day to day in constant fear.

Gabriel Richard, heartbroken at the turn of events, tried to maintain a calm he did not feel. He did what he could to ease the burden of all the people of the village.

Following Hull's surrender, Richard and Father Marchand, pastor of Assumption parish on the Canadian side of the river, visited Colonel Procter. Marchand, a Canadian and therefore not a captive, was also quite pro-British. Richard was at least thoroughly American, if not actually anti-British.

Procter was unemotional as he received the two priests. He was extremely polite almost to the point of rudeness.

"There will be rules, Mr. Richard," he said. "These rules are meant to be kept. By everyone."

Richard realized this was intended to remind him that he was included. But he said nothing.

"So long as the rules are obeyed there will be no countermeasures taken against your people," Procter concluded.

"My people know the conditions that exist," Richard said finally. "If their rights are protected, and their property, they will violate no just rule."

"Law recognizes no excuse, Mr. Richard," Procter snapped. "Those in defeat have no rights."

Procter made no effort, it seems, to give protection of any kind. The Indians were allowed to roam the streets, to plunder homes, and to destroy property. Nothing was done to stop the destruction.

Not even St. Anne's church was safe from the marauding Indians. One obviously drunken group invaded the church and tore the pipes from Richard's precious organ. They walked through the streets, blowing the pipes nosily as though they were horns. The din and the racket were horrible to hear.

Finally one of the French citizens could stand the noise no longer. He told one Indian that when one of the organ pipes were blown the Great Spirit might become displeased since the pipes were part of the Great Spirit's flute. The Indian told another Indian. The word spread. Before many hours had passed, every pipe had been restored to the organ in St. Anne's church.

The church was safe but plundering throughout the town continued. Richard saw Indians burning

116

buildings with nothing done to stop them. He saw them bring children to their parents and offer them for ransom. He was sickened by the sight of Indians shouting through the streets as they waved bloody scalps.

He had intended to maintain silence as far as he could. But he could keep quiet no longer. He spoke out against the atrocities and demanded that the authorities control the Indians.

Procter listened and did nothing. The people themselves came close to open rebellion. Richard openly defended the citizens when Procter warned them of arrest.

In January of 1813, a small American army contingent was defeated at River Raisin. Three hundred of the prisoners were massacred by the Indians while others were held for ransom. These were taken through the streets of Detroit and offered for sale to anyone who would put up the money. Richard led a group of citizens who provided ransom for every prisoner. Procter merely stood by and watched the proceedings.

This was too much for the citizens of Detroit. Their anger exploded into a series of demonstrations.

Procter declared martial law. Thirty of Detroit's

more prominent citizens were arrested and exiled. For some unknown reason, Father Richard was not one of them. He was left free.

If Procter thought that imprisoning the thirty men might quiet the priest, he was wrong. Richard's condemnation of Procter and his vicious, inhuman handling of his assignment as commander of the defeated Americans left nothing to the imagination.

Procter threatened Richard with arrest. He demanded that the priest take an oath of allegiance to the British Crown.

"I have taken one oath to support the Constitution of the United States," Richard told Procter. "I cannot take another. Do with me as you please."

Procter ordered Richard's arrest. The priest was removed from Detroit and taken across the river where he was imprisoned at Fort Malden.

Word of Richard's arrest spread quickly. The great Indian chief, Tecumseh, leader of the confederation of Indian tribes, heard of it and stormed into Procter's office. Tecumseh demanded that Father Richard be released.

"If you do not free our Black Coat immediately," Tecumseh threatened, "I will return with all my warriors to the home of our fathers in the Wabash coun-

Jailed by the British

try, and you English will fight alone against your white brothers."

Procter was uncertain what to do. To release Richard would be a show of weakness on his part. Not to release him would make an enemy of Tecumseh, and Procter was afraid of the powerful Indian chief. Besides, his instructions from the British high command were to give the Indians no cause to doubt the English.

Taking Father Marchand and a prominent Canadian with him as witnesses, Procter went to Fort Malden and faced Gabriel Richard. Knowing he had no choice but to release the priest, he tried to save face by offering Richard a choice.

"Do as you please," he told Richard. "Sign this pledge that you will not speak out against the Crown, that you will keep your thoughts to yourself, and I will set you free in the custody of Father Marchand. Or you must leave Detroit."

With a choice of either exile or restraining himself from expressing any open opinions, Richard chose the latter. His people needed him. He could not leave them alone while such tragedies as the British occupation under Procter faced them. With Father Marchand and the Canadian witnessing the document, he signed the pledge not to speak out against the British.

Not long after Richard's release, the British fleet was scuttled by Oliver Hazard Perry in the Battle of Lake Erie. Then General William Henry Harrison marched on Detroit in preparation for an invasion of Canada.

Procter realized he could not withstand a battle with Harrison's forces and evacuated Fort Lernault and Detroit, taking his army eastward into Canada. Chief Tecumseh, made a brigadier general by the English, helped cover Procter's forces as they retreated across the Detroit River and across the Canadian farmlands.

General Harrison caught up with the Indians and British before they had retreated fifty miles, backing them up against the Thames River in Ontario. The British and Indian armies were completely overwhelmed. Procter, in a final example of the cowardice that had marked his command at Detroit, deserted his men and fled. Chief Tecumseh fought to the bitter end, refusing to surrender, and was finally killed.

Peace returned to Michigan, and Father Gabriel Richard could go back to his work.

CHAPTER **14**

AFTERMATH OF WAR

The war was over. The suffering was not.

Father Gabriel Richard looked at what was left of his beloved Detroit and Michigan and his heart was torn with compassion and pity.

The streets of the city and the fields of the countryside were naked. His people had been without homes and without food before. But the terror and devastation of the fire left nothing like the scar which forms as a result of man's inhumanity to man.

This time there seemed no place to which he could

turn for help for his starving people. After the fire, food came from the farms up and down either side of the river. Brother helped brother in that disaster.

But now even the farms were bare. The farmers had been unable to plant their crops during the years of the fighting and the occupation of the territory by the British. So there was no corn or wheat, nothing from which flour or meal could be ground. There was not even grass or hay on the fields on which cattle might have grazed. So there was no meat.

And there was little clothing. The Indians had stripped the citizens of all but what they wore on their backs, so that when the cold months came there was more suffering for those who had already suffered beyond all endurance.

Richard suffered with his people but he was hardly conscious of his own discomfort. There was so much work to be done, so much help to be given.

The only ray of hope for a better future came from the fact that, by the end of the war, Governor Hull had been replaced. His cowardly actions at the surrender of Detroit had finally brought action from Washington.

Lewis Cass was the new territorial governor. Cass was strong where Hull had been weak. Where Hull could not make up his mind and would delay action through fear of doing the wrong thing, Cass had a sharp mind which got to the core of a problem quickly and was as quick to act. And Cass was a good, humane administrator.

Richard had worked with Lewis Cass and he knew him. He said a prayer of gratitude when word came of his appointment. But he also knew that many months would pass before Cass could do anything about the suffering and devastation.

While there was peace around Detroit and along the Canadian border, there was still fighting elsewhere. General Andrew Jackson had not yet fought the Battle of New Orleans.

Cass could not yet take over his post as governor. The young United States was still too busy supplying the armies which would soon crush the British and drive them away once and for all. The people had no one to turn to but Gabriel Richard.

Richard was fortunate that he had at least one sympathetic official with whom he might work. This was Judge Woodward. Between them, Judge Augustus Woodward and Father Gabriel Richard worked night and day to organize emergency help and to get food and clothing for those who were in dire need.

Woodward wasted no time in advising the Secretary of War of conditions in Detroit. Busy with the war or not, the Secretary had to listen. Woodward detailed the starvation of the people in all the Michigan area, even to reporting that the "inhabitants of the River Raisin have been obliged to resort to chopp'd hay, boiled, for subsistence."

"I would humbly suggest to the government," Woodward told the Secretary of War, "to allow a supply of provisions to the amount of a thousand dollars to be purchased at Erie in Pennsylvania and transmitted to this place for the relief of the Territory generally; to be distributed by the Commandant on the certificate of the Roman Catholic Clergyman, a gentleman of the firmest patriotism. . . ."

The high regard which Judge Woodward showed for Richard was matched by Governor Cass when he gave orders for the distribution of the relief goods which came in answer to Woodward's request. Catholics in the area—and there were few who were not—would be given food and clothing if their request was signed by "the Revd. Mr. Richard."

Speaking of the relief, Cass said, in explaining the regulations which would determine distribution: "In extending it to the people of the Territory, I consulted with the Catholic Rector whose ecclesiastical Jurisdiction comprehended the whole country, and whose character as well as office gives to his representations upon this subject great weight. To him I have committed the task of distribution . . ."

But food and clothing to satisfy immediate needs was not enough. The future had also to be taken care of so that the fields and the farms which had grown such fine crops before could again yield the grain and vegetables and fruits which had been so plentiful.

Governor Cass, pressed by Judge Woodward as well as Father Richard, asked again and again for cattle and seeds with which the farms might be re-stocked. These finally arrived in time for a crop to be harvested in 1815. The distribution of this, too, was in the hands of Gabriel Richard.

Slowly, and inspired by Richard's constant cheer-fulness and words of hope, the despair of the people was replaced by confidence in better things to come. Everyone worked together for the common good. Detroit was coming through a second great disaster.

Richard knew human nature. He realized that once the hardships of starvation had faded the people might forget that it was a compassionate government which had come to their rescue. Even worse, they might take such help so much for granted that, should even the smallest disaster again strike, they would look to others for help and not help themselves.

He determined to imprint as indelibly as possible

United as Americans

on the minds of the people the source of their help and the object of their gratitude. On January 14, 1816, he held a meeting of all his parishioners.

Richard spoke to his people warmly and prayerfully. He suggested that they pass a resolution giving thanks to God and to the authorities who had helped them through the trying times of the past. Richard, himself, helped write the resolution.

It called on Governor Cass, who "is himself entitled to the Gratitude of the Inhabitants," to express to the President of the United States on behalf of all the people of the Territory of Michigan "the high sense they entertain of the innumerable favors received from the Bounty of the Government during his administration."

Stirred by Richard's own sincerity and moved by their own sense of gratitude, the meeting passed the resolution amid wild cheers.

A new day had been born for Detroit. Never again would there be distrust between the English- and the French-speaking elements. Both had worked together through famine and starvation. Henceforth, they would think of themselves only as Americans.

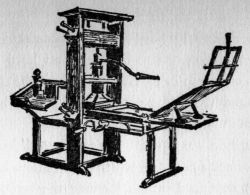

CHAPTER **15**

FATHER OF MICHIGAN EDUCATION

Perhaps it began after his fall from the scaffolding years before at his school in Saintes. Certainly a change had come over Gabriel Richard after he had recovered from his injuries, and it may be that his great interest in learning began in those hours and days he spent lying on his back.

It may have begun in the Illinois country or during his early days in the Michigan Territory as he saw Indian and Frenchman alike struggling to make a living, the struggle so much harder because they had had no education and could neither read nor write.

Wherever it may have started, Gabriel Richard's deep conviction that to live one must learn and his tireless efforts to bring education to all the children, Indian and white alike, played a vital part in the progress that came to the frontier.

Education was especially necessary to help the Indian become a peaceful, worthwhile citizen. His civilization depended on his learning the ways of the white man, on his accepting them, and converting them to his own way of living.

In 1808 a school was already being built on the Canadian side of the river, opposite Detroit. Richard brought this to the attention of Governor Hull and Judges Woodward and Bates. It would be a sin against all the American people, Richard pointed out, if their children were deprived of at least as much learning as the Canadians.

The authorities had to agree with Richard. How could they do otherwise? But it was left to the priest to do most of the planning and to fight for action so that his plans might mean something.

He had established his little school at Spring Hill. He had lost it and began again at another farm. Richard could never give up when it came to helping his people to a better life.

In 1811, during moments of near despair when he

had lost Spring Hill, he wrote to Thomas Jefferson in retirement at Monticello. "I have not given up," he wrote the former President, "and will not give up the design of instructing Indian children."

Richard's great dream for educating the children of Michigan must have been inspired by his knowledge of the French system put into practice by Napoleon. Under this plan all education was subsidized by the State. It began with the teaching of the youngest in the lower grades, then progress into an academy or kind of high school and finally into a college or university.

In 1816, John Monteith, Michigan's first Protestant minister, came to Detroit. Richard lost no time in calling on the Reverend Monteith, helping him find a building in which he might hold his services and, in general, giving the Protestant every help he could to get established.

Though their religions were far apart in beliefs and though the two men were themselves so different in nature and temperament, Richard and Monteith became close friends. They would sit for hours talking over their dreams, their hopes, and their plans.

Richard soon found that Monteith's ideas of education were much like his own. Sometime during one of their conversations the idea of a territorial educational system, one designed along the lines of the French plan, must have come up. Richard and Monteith took their idea to Governor Cass and Judge Woodward.

The governor and the judge had both taught school in their younger days. They had thoughts of their own, and the final plan certainly must have been the combined thinking of at least all four men. Judge Woodward, as the legal expert, was asked to put the plan into the form of a resolution which might be drafted into a law.

As it was finally approved on August 26, 1817, the act as drawn up by Judge Woodward established what he called "the Catholepistemiad," which meant, roughly, a school system of universal sciences. It would be later recognized as the University of Michigan, the first state university in the United States.

Judge Woodward, no doubt with the help of both Richard and Monteith, had divided the proposed courses into thirteen departments covering almost every field of learning. These departments ranged from literature and grammar, and all branches of mathematics, through all areas of the sciences, philosophy, astronomy, history, medicine, law, and theology.

It was a design far ahead of its time, and many years would pass before the entire plan would be put into operation. But it was a great beginning and finally brought legal recognition for Richard's efforts to establish a good educational system.

Under the plan there would be a head of each of the thirteen branches of learning and the system would be supervised by these heads. Here, for the first time, would be an educational institution operated by its teachers.

At the beginning, the thirteen departments were divided between Richard and Monteith, the Catholic taking six, the Protestant clergyman seven. Monteith was president; Richard, vice-president. Later, when Monteith left Detroit to return East, Richard became president.

A two-story building, twenty-four feet by fifty feet, was constructed in the heart of the city not far from the site agreed on for the new St. Anne's church.

Richard, realizing that learning had to be made available for the outlying districts as well as Detroit, suggested that elementary schools be established in the River Raisin area as well as at Mackinac. Monteith agreed and the schools were started, the principal subjects taught being grammar, arithmetic and reading.

133

The Detroit elementary school, located on the ground floor of the new building, was opened on August 10, 1818. At the same time, since the second floor was not yet finished, another location was used for the classical academy which would teach more advanced courses in French, Latin and Greek. Instructors were hired for both of the schools, and Richard and Monteith confined their efforts to supervising the schools in Detroit and outlying districts.

Richard's great dream had come true. He could be called in truth "Father of Michigan Education."

CHAPTER 16

FINALLY, A NEW ST. ANNE'S

It must not be supposed that Gabriel Richard, teacher and educator, or Gabriel Richard, printer and civic leader, ever played a minor role to Father Gabriel Richard, priest and missionary. Not for a minute, whatever other obligations there may have been at any time, did he cease to be a man of God, dedicated to bringing a better life to anyone under his influence.

No disillusionment or disappointment, and there were many, was ever allowed to interfere with his principal work. The split in his congregation was never completely healed even though he had delayed the building of the new church he so desperately needed and wanted.

When Bishop Flaget came from Bardstown to Detroit in 1818, he stopped any open grumblings by making the decision that the new St. Anne's would be located on the site chosen by Richard.

Some money was already available for the construction. After the fire which had destroyed the old church, and while he was in the process of planning for the new, Richard accepted contributions not only from his own parishioners but also in some of the eastern cities he visited while buying the printing press and the organ and harpsichord.

In 1814 Richard received a letter from John R. Williams, a prominent member of his congregation and the man who would one day be Detroit's first mayor. Williams was in Albany at the time and he asked his pastor's consent to ask for contributions in that city and in eastern New York State.

When Bishop Flaget arrived in Detroit, Richard had at least enough with which to begin construction of the church. The bishop asked to go over Richard's plans for the building.

Flaget was both farsighted and practical. He could foresee the time when Detroit would become the seat of the diocese of Michigan. Then St. Anne's would serve as the cathedral. The bishop felt that Richard's specifications of a church eighty-seven feet long by sixty feet wide would not do. He suggested that the length be increased to one hundred and sixteen feet.

Richard was dumfounded. His estimated costs were already so high he could not see where enough money could be raised to pay for the completed building. Worried almost to the point of fright, Richard agreed to the expanded structure.

Perhaps to make sure that the plans were not changed after he left—or perhaps to put a definite stop to talk about any other location—Bishop Flaget decided to lay the cornerstone of the new church while he was still in Detroit. This he did on Tuesday, June 9. The new St. Anne's was finally taking shape, thirteen years less two days after the old had been destroyed by fire.

Progress was painfully slow. Materials, both stone and lumber, were hard to come by. And they were expensive.

The Detroit *Gazette*, which had after a time replaced Richard's own Michigan *Essay* as the city's newspaper, carried an advertisement in its issue of August 18, almost two and a half months after the laying of the cornerstone.

"Great Bargain!" the ad read. "Offered by Gabriel

Richard, rector of St. Anne's. 200 hard dollars will be be given for twenty toises [a toise measures a little over two yards] of long stone, of Stony Island, delivered at Detroit, on the wharf of Mr. Jacob Smith, or two hundred and forty dollars if delivered on the church ground. 100 barrels of lime are wanted immediately. Five shillings will be given per barrel at the riverside, and six shillings delivered on the church ground."

Even if help to supervise the building was available, Richard could not have afforded it. So he acted as architect, supplier, and contractor. His delays, naturally, were doubled and tripled, as were his troubles.

The war had not been over very long, and the city, still a frontier town, had not fully recovered from the aftereffects of the struggle. There was a shortage of currency in the area.

As a result, Richard had to pay his workmen with his own scrip. This was a type of paper substitute for money commonly called a "shinplaster." Richard was having his scrip, or shinplasters, printed at the office of the Detroit *Gazette*.

One of the printers stole the type one night when the newspaper office was closed. He ran off a good supply of the counterfeit scrip and forged Richard's name to them. Then he proceeded to pass them off all around the Territory.

Richard was architect and contractor.

No one knows exactly how much false scrip was passed off by the printer. He got away by enlisting in the army and leaving the Territory before the counterfeiting was discovered.

Richard, however, was crushed. He could not imagine how anyone could have done such a dishonest act. Nor could he allow any of the people who had been innocently victimized into accepting the counterfeits to be cheated. There is no way of knowing how much of his precious time was taken up in rounding up all the false shinplasters and repaying the victims in full.

As soon as he learned of the counterfeiting, he had the following notice published in the city paper:

"The Undersigned returns his thanks to the merchants and other citizens of Detroit and its vicinity for the liberal assistance given him in erecting the Church of St. Anne, and having given free circulation to his small notes.

"With sorrow and displeasure, he has discovered that many of his small notes are counterfeited, and that several of his neighbors have suffered by reason of the counterfeit. It appears that more than 200 fifty-cent bills have been within the past fortnight put in circulation in this city."

It was a lengthy explanation of the evil done and being done, as well as an assurance that no one would lose one cent by reason of the escaped printer's dishonesty. The notice concluded with:

"The public are warned that every possible exertion will be made by the undersigned to redeem his bills without delay, and in order to do away with any fears that may exist as to his capability to do so, he deems it proper to state that, besides three valuable lots in the city, the Corporation of St. Anne holds a very valuable and extensive spot of ground which surrounds the church, which is worth ten times more than the whole amount of the bills now in circulation."

He was pledging all the property and all the assets of his church!

Stone by stone the building took shape. By Christmas two years after the start, the walls were about eight feet off the ground and roofed over so that services could be held in the basement. Then the upper floor, also walled with stone, was added. A double door at the front entrance was reached by a flight of steps leading to a portico supported by graceful twin pillars.

The bell which had summoned the early pioneers to Mass in the first St. Anne's had been saved and would be placed in one of the twin towers which were to rise above the church. The pulpit and two side altars had also escaped the fire and would be installed in the main church when it was completed.

But that was still some years in the future.

After Father Dilhet's return to Baltimore many years before, Richard was almost always alone in serving the vast territory that was his church responsibility. Occasionally a visiting missionary would stop in Detroit and help out for a week or two. But seldom did he have any help for a longer period than that.

When Bishop Flaget visited Detroit for the laying of the cornerstone of the new St. Anne's, he brought two young priests, Father John Bertrand and Father Philip Janvier with him. Both of these young men were impressed with Father Richard's devotion to his people. Both recognized the hardships under which he worked, almost always alone and with such a wide territory to cover.

The two young priests asked the bishop's permission to remain and assist Richard. He readily assented.

With two assistants to aid him, Richard was now able to give renewed attention to the outlying missions. Mackinac, Sault Ste. Marie, River Raisin, and the missions north and east of Detroit along the St. Clair River and lake were not weighing as heavily on his mind.

The new help also freed Richard to engage in other activities occasioned by the fast progress being made in the entire Territory as a result of Governor Cass's leadership. The addition of Ohio, Indiana, and Illinois as States had called for a revision of boundaries. The Michigan district now comprised all that remained of the Northwest Territory and this included all of what is now Michigan and Wisconsin as well as part of northern Minnesota. This also represented the extent of Richard's responsibility as a priest.

More and more people were leaving the eastern seaboard states and migrating to Detroit and Michigan. Travel was becoming easier and faster. On August 27, 1818, the *Walk-in-the-Water*, the first steamboat to sail the Great Lakes, docked at Detroit. There was already talk of a great canal called "Erie" which would connect the Hudson River with Lake Erie and make it possible to travel by water from New York City to Detroit, then to Mackinac and around to Chicago.

In July of 1819, Michigan was able to send William Woodbridge to Washington as its first territorial delegate in Congress. Then, under the direction of Governor Cass, a new treaty with the Indians was concluded which gave Michigan full title to the eastern half of its lower peninsula.

Richard, whom the Indians trusted completely, was involved in many of the treaty negotiations. He was therefore invited by the Pottawatami tribe to join the treaty council to be held in Chicago at which the sale of Indian lands in southwestern Michigan would be discussed. The chief of the Pottawatamies wanted Richard's help in establishing a mission and setting up school arrangements for the Pottawatami reservation.

Since Bishop Flaget had already asked Richard to visit the northern settlements of Mackinac and Sault Ste. Marie, which Richard was anxious to do, he accepted the invitation of the Pottawatamies. He could accomplish everything in the one trip.

Richard left Detroit on July 4 and sailed first to Mackinac. It was the first visit of a priest since Father Dilhet's visit fifteen years before. Richard remained in Mackinac three weeks before going on to Sault Ste. Marie.

He then headed back through the straits of Mackinac and into Lake Michigan. Bad weather forced him ashore at the mouth of the Marquette River on the east bank of the lake. There a group of Ottawa Indians showed him where Father Marquette, the Jesuit missionary, had died in 1674.

The Ottawas had loved Marquette, who was a kindly, saintly priest. Richard endeared himself to

144

them by saying Mass on the spot pointed out to him. The Indians told Richard that the cross which had marked the place of Marquette's death had been blown down three years before. A Catholic who was traveling with Richard made a new cross which Richard erected and blessed in the presence of eight Ottawa Indians.

More bad weather delayed Richard's arrival in Chicago. By the time he reached the city at the southern extremity of Lake Michigan, the treaty had already been signed and arrangements for a mission had been completed with a Baptist minister who had accompanied the white negotiators.

Grieved by his failure, Richard planned his return home. Then, since he could get no boat passage for two months, he decided he might visit his old settlements on the Mississippi and then return to Detroit by the route he had originally taken up the Ohio to the Wabash River and then to Detroit.

He stopped in St. Louis, then visited Cahokia, Kaskaskia, and Prairie du Rocher, finally starting for Detroit on horseback. On the way to Vincennes, Richard was thrown from his horse and badly injured. Though he was alone he managed somehow to get to Vincennes where he was delayed about two weeks while his injuries healed.

While he was laid up in Vincennes, Richard decided to turn south into Kentucky and pay Bishop Flaget and his own diocesan seat a visit. He reached Bardstown in time to take part in the consecration of a new bishop for the Michigan Territory. The diocese of Cincinnati, with jurisdiction over Michigan, had just been created with Edward Fenwick named as its bishop.

In Bardstown Richard became acquainted with Father Anthony Ganilh, a newly ordained priest, and with Francis Badin, who had recently left the seminary. Both young men found great interest in Richard's work. Father Ganilh asked and received Bishop Flaget's permission to go with Richard to Detroit. Young Badin accompanied them as far as Cincinnati, by which time he had made up his mind. Bishop Fenwick, who had returned to Cincinnati to take up his duties, ordained Badin. The three priests then returned to Detroit.

Father Ganilh was assigned to the mission at River Raisin, and young Father Badin remained at St. Anne's as an assistant.

The widespread parish over which Father Gabriel presided now enjoyed help such as it had never had. And the pastor of the new St. Anne's could become involved in the politics of the day.

146

CHAPTER **17**

A CRUEL BUSINESS

William Woodbridge, who had been Michigan's first territorial delegate to Congress, resigned after a year. Solomon Sibley, appointed to serve Woodbridge's unexpired term, was elected to a full period in office, then decided he did not want re-election. This left the field wide open for the election of 1823.

The most prominent candidates among the seven or eight who announced their intention of running for the post were John R. Williams, one of Father Richard's parishioners and a great help to Richard in soliciting funds for building the new church, Austin Wing, who was County Sheriff, and John Biddle, a member of the famous Biddle family of Philadelphia, who first came to Detroit as a soldier and remained as an Indian agent.

The campaign had been under way for a few weeks. The three men had been bitterly attacking each other. Then one night two prominent citizens of Detroit knocked at Father Richard's door. Richard opened the door and invited them in.

"Father Richard," one of the men said to the priest, "we believe that if you become a candidate for election as delegate to Congress you will win."

Richard looked in disbelief at the two men. The second man, also a Frenchman, made it even stronger.

"We French are being outnumbered with so many strangers moving into the territory," he said. "We need someone in Congress whom we can trust. Someone who will look out for our interests. That is you, Father."

Richard had never had any great personal interest in politics. What he had done and what association he had had with any person in authority had been either on the basis of friendship, as with Justice Woodward, or to protect the interests of his people.

Richard stared at the men for a moment through

his dark, deep-set eyes. It was preposterous! Was this some kind of joke these men were playing? He, a priest of God, engaging in the not always gentle or fair field of politics? He became angry.

"Be off with you," he shouted. "Go! It is folly to even think of such a thing!"

The two men left, but not before one of them turned and said: "Think it over, Father Richard. You may think differently of it later."

Richard closed the door behind them, his eyes blazing. He thought for a moment and the anger faded. It *was* a joke. It had to be a joke. Richard began to laugh aloud.

Father Badin, coming into the hall from his room, found him still amused by what had happened. When Richard explained what had happened, Father Badin, too, thought it amusing. But he also thought it a great compliment.

During the following few days, the subject came up many times as the two priests sat together for their meals or relaxed for a moment in the common room. Each time it was discussed, it became less amusing and more a possibility.

Father Badin reminded Richard that as a territorial delegate he would spend much time in Washington and mix with many of the most influential members

149

of the government. Badin said, "How could you better further your plans for education for the people and for more missions for the Indians?"

As the days went by, Father Richard found himself more and more inclined to accept the nomination. Yet he was not sure and so would not make his wishes known. Finally he wrote to an old and trusted friend of his days at the seminary in Issy who was now in St. Louis, Bishop Louis Duborg, and asked his advice. Bishop Duborg answered immediately.

"It seems to me that Providence designs to use this extraordinary means to help you and the Church in your district," the bishop wrote. "I hope that you have decided in the affirmative, and I would rejoice if my letter arrived in time to allay the fears that you might feel in accepting, and to inspire you with the confidence that such duties demand."

Reading the bishop's letter, Richard made up his mind. He would offer his name as candidate for the office of territorial delegate.

His announcement was met with cheers from most of the citizens of Detroit and especially from his parishioners. He left Detroit on a trip to Mackinac, Green Bay, and other northern missions to explain to the people there his reasons for taking the step.

Once he was away from Detroit, the other three

The would-be congressman faced cheers and bitterness.

candidates ceased their attacks on each other. All three turned their wrath on Richard. What right had this priest to enter the contest, they demanded, each giving a different answer as it suited his campaign and personality.

The most bitter of the three was Richard's friend and parishioner, John R. Williams. Williams accused Richard of using politics as a means of getting himself elevated to the rank of bishop. He was so incensed at a priest mixing in politics that he and his rich uncle, Joseph Campeau, left the Catholic church for good.

The *Gazette*, the only newspaper in the territory, was taken over by the other two candidates. Naturally, then, the paper never mentioned Richard as a candidate and many of the voters never knew that he was running for the office.

Word then was spread that Richard was, in fact, ineligible for the office since he had never been naturalized as a citizen. This was true but hardly unusual. Like many others before and after, he had come to the frontier country in its early days and had never thought much about it.

Richard came before a Judge Fletcher and made application for citizenship. Fletcher, who was campaign manager for one of the candidates as well as presiding judge of the county court, ruled that he lacked authority in such matters as citizenship. He suggested that Richard take his application to either the district or the supreme court. He failed to say that neither of these was in session.

This was so obviously a political maneuver by Judge Fletcher that the public was up in arms. Richard was induced to renew his application before the two other judges of the county court. Fletcher was over-ridden, and Richard was granted citizenship in the United States he had served so well.

When the election returns were counted, Gabriel Richard had won with a total of 444 votes. Biddle had received 421, Wing, 335, and John R. Williams only 51 votes.

Biddle, who had run second to Richard, did not immediately give up the fight. When Richard made his appearance in Washington for the opening session of the Eighteenth Congress, Biddle was already there protesting that Richard should not be given his seat. The priest, Biddle contended, was not qualified for the post since he had not been a citizen for a full year.

A House committee investigating Biddle's charges ruled against him and declared that Father Gabriel Richard had been duly elected and was eligible for the post to which he had been elected.

So it was that Gabriel Richard, the missionary who had come from France with the expectation of returning there, became the only Catholic priest ever to be a member of the United States Congress.

The Washington which saw much of Gabriel Richard for the next two years was young and unfinished. Pennsylvania Avenue, that now broad boulevard that connects the Capitol with the White House, was little different from an ordinary country road, narrow and dirty.

James Monroe was in his second term as President and seemed to enjoy the many visits the black-coated priest made to the White House, visits during which Richard told many stories of his encounters with the Indians. John Calhoun, secretary of war in Monroe's cabinet, also entertained Richard quite often, drawing from him his many hopes for the Indian schools and missions which were still Richard's unfulfilled dream.

During his first session in Congress, there was little that Richard actually accomplished. He returned for the second session just in time to take part in a great celebration honoring the Marquis de Lafayette, as the great French hero of the American Revolution revisited the United States.

154

That second session of Congress gave Richard an opportunity to support a work that had been dear to him for many years. In Detroit his heart had been touched by the many deaf-mutes, and he was so determined to help them that he sent Elizabeth Lyons, a lay teacher who worked for Richard and would later become an Ursuline nun, to New York to study the system for teaching the deaf as originated by Abbé Sicard of France.

In January, 1825, he introduced a bill which would provide funds for teaching "the Deaf and Dumb of Kentucky, New York, Pennsylvania, and of the Territory of Michigan." His hopes were high as he introduced the bill and he felt that he had furthered the cause of unfortunates who had no one to help them. The bill, however, never got out of committee. Richard's only satisfaction was that he had tried.

Richard's greatest, and perhaps only real, success as a congressional delegate was his effort in promotion of the Territory's greatest need—good, usable highways. Actually, the first good road between Detroit and Chicago was the direct result of his work.

In his two years in Congress, Richard made one truly moving and important speech. This talk, promoting the highway which he declared would be of national, not local, importance, was so well thought out, so dramatically conceived, that there seemed little doubt of the bill's passage.

Richard told the members of the House of Representatives that the proposed road would be in effect an extension of the Erie Canal that would connect the heart of the growing United States with the harbor at New York.

"Make this road now while you have the full sovereignty over the Territory of Michigan, before it becomes an independent State, and you may easily anticipate how beneficial this road will be to your finances," he said to the assembled House. "There are more than seventeen million acres of generally good and fertile land in Michigan proper, without speaking of the ninety-four million acres in the Northwest Territory. Without a road to go into these lands, they have no value. We are credibly informed that on our inland seas . . . no less than one hundred and fifty vessels are plying up and down, on board of which whole families do come sometimes with their wagons, horses, sheep, and milk cows, land in Detroit, ready to go in search of good land, to settle on it, and having their money ready to give to the receiver of the land office. No road to go into that immense wilderness! What a disappointment!"

He explained that the road would cost veritably nothing, that it would pay for itself through revenues taken through sale of the lands along the right of way. And he pointed out how important such a road would be also to military operations.

The bill was passed with minimum debate. An appropriation of three thousand dollars to start work on the road was included.

Richard returned to Detroit satisfied that he had accomplished at least some good for his people and his Territory. He anticipated being re-elected and returning to Washington for the opening of the Nineteenth Congress.

Even before he arrived in Detroit, the campaign to unseat him had started. His opposition candidates were again John Biddle and Sheriff Austin Wing, and these two, aided by a still bitter John R. Williams, who was interested only in defeating Richard, had already started a campaign to discredit Richard.

Pulling out all stops, reading letters designed to belittle him, using such tactics as moving up election day to a time when French trappers would be in the fields and lose their vote, they stacked the odds against the priest.

Richard voters were challenged at the polls and refused their vote because they had not paid their poll tax. Others were allowed to cast their ballot whether or not the tax had been paid. French voters who did go to the polls were clubbed. Ballots cast for Richard, but deposited in the wrong box, were thrown out. Those for the opposition, though also in the wrong box, were counted.

Despite all these measures, the opposition was almost upset. The final vote showed that Austin Wing had polled 728 votes. Richard was a very close second with 724. Biddle ran third with 684.

Richard had lost, and he was again defeated at the next election, in 1827. His name was entered in 1829 but most likely without his consent. He made no campaign and was never in the contest.

Gabriel Richard had found politics to be a vicious game and in no way to his liking.

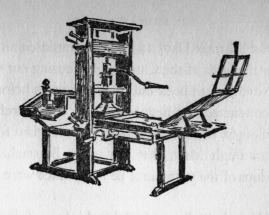

CHAPTER 18

THE CRUELEST BLOW

By the early 1830's, Richard was again settled in his duties as church administrator for the Michigan country, greatly relieved to be finished with the disheartening hypocrisy of politics. Much had already been accomplished. So much more was yet to be done.

The twin steeples of the now finished new St. Anne's pierced the sky high above Detroit as a symbol of continued hope. So often had he been discouraged during the years of planning and building. Yet here it was, completed.

On Christmas Day, 1828, with music commemorating the birth of the Christ child pouring out of the organ which had been only a whim years before, he had conducted the first services in the church. He had thought then, as he robed in the sacristy for the Solemn High Mass, that the many heartaches and hardships of the years since he left France were nothing.

This made it all worthwhile—this beautiful church of stone, and what it represented. It would still stand long after he had gone to account for his life to God.

On that Christmas Day as he faced his congregation to sing out a resounding "Dominus Vobiscum," Gabriel Richard might have seen only his new church filled to overflowing as a symbol of his accomplishment in the Michigan country. But his touch was that moment being felt in every settlement throughout the Territory.

So many new missions had been established in addition to those at River Raisin, Mackinac, and Sault Ste. Marie. So many more little churches had been built. As far away as Prairie du Chien in the Wisconsin country. At Green Bay. Along the shores of Lake Michigan and along the banks of the St. Joseph River. At St. Ignace and Marquette and L'Arbre Croche. In all of these, they would be celebrating the birth of the Prince of Peace, red man and white man side by side.

But what Gabriel Richard would not likely have thought was that each mission and each church was almost literally a product of his mind and hand. It had not been an easy task, but the accomplishment was there.

In the early years, Richard had worked almost always alone. Once the growth of the Michigan country became apparent, he had help, some valuable, some questionable. And recently the most able assistance of all had come in the person of a young Austrian, Father Frederic Baraga.

Placing Father Baraga in charge of the northern country, the area above and below the straits of Mackinac, had been a stroke of luck. Baraga had the same regard and affection for the Indian as Richard had. The red men believed in him and trusted him as they had the "Black Robe."

In the years immediately following Richard's retirement from politics, the Michigan Territory was under the jurisdiction of the Ohio diocese, supervised from Cincinnati by Bishop Edward Fenwick. But the establishment of so many new missions in the Michigan, Minnesota and Wisconsin areas of the Michigan

The Indians trusted Richard and the new "Black Robe."

Territory was making the job most unwieldy for the bishop of Cincinnati. It was time that Michigan was a diocese in itself.

Actually this had been talked about in Baltimore, in Bardstown and in Cincinnati. Ambrose Maréchal, who had left France with Richard and two other priests aboard the brigantine *La Reine des Coeurs*, had succeeded John Carroll and was now Archbishop of Baltimore and reigning prelate in the United States.

Bishop Fenwick had come to Detroit years before to look over the possibilities of carving a new diocese with that city as its seat. After his visit, he had written the Archbishop:

"Nothing could afford me more pleasure and relief of mind than the erection of the bishop's See in Detroit, whose jurisdiction should extend over the Michigan and Northwest Territories, containing an extent of country equal to all Europe."

Who would be named bishop of Detroit? Who could best administer this territory, "an extent of country equal to all Europe?"

This was a question which hardly needed an answer. None could possibly be more qualified than the man who almost single-handedly had fashioned the diocese out of the wilderness.

Who more than Gabriel Richard deserved being named the first bishop of Detroit?

Before Richard's misfortune in politics, Bishop Fenwick had gone to Rome and outlined the plans for the new diocese. He suggested that the first bishop of Detroit be none other than Gabriel Richard. Fenwick produced letters from the most prominent laity in the area, including letters from both Joseph Campeau and John R. Williams written, of course, before they stormed out of the Catholic Church when Richard announced his entrance into politics.

Williams' letter was especially praising. He wrote: "Your diocesans being likewise informed that it is in contemplation to create a separate Bishopric in the Territory of Michigan beg leave respectfully to mention the name of our Reverend and well-beloved Pastor, Gabriel Richard, and humbly recommend him as a suitable person to fill that distinguished station. His long and pious services, indefatigible zeal, and charitable character entitle him to our sincere admiration, respect and eternal gratitude."

This from the man who, a short time later, would accuse Richard of reaching for the bishop's mitre with one hand while grasping a congressional seat with the other.

Bishop Fenwick returned to Detroit without the appointment having been made or the diocese created. Month followed month and no word was received.

Finally the news came. Detroit would become a diocese along the lines proposed by Bishop Fenwick. Pope Leo XII had named Father Gabriel Richard to be Detroit's first bishop.

Richard was humble and overjoyed. There was so much more he could do with the authority which would come with the new assignment. How much easier it would be to care for his beloved Indians as well as serve his own people!

Congratulations came to him from Baltimore, Bardstown, and Cincinnati, as well as from New York and Boston. Perhaps the most welcome might have been the simple smile and handclasp of the young Austrian, Frederic Baraga, who would himself later become first bishop of the Michigan northern country.

Day followed day and as each dawned Richard expected to receive the official confirmation of his appointment from the Holy Father. Disturbed by the delay, Archbishop Maréchal wrote to Rome from Baltimore. Bishop Fenwick wrote from Cincinnati. Still no word came.

What had actually happened no one knows. It could be that the now disgruntled John R. Williams and his rich, influential uncle, Joseph Campeau, had themselves written Rome. It might be that the authorities in the Vatican became worried over appointing a priest who had been involved in so much controversy with his parishioners. Perhaps it was the large debts which Richard had incurred in building his new St. Anne's.

March 20, 1827, the diocese was officially born. But it was a diocese without a bishop, and the Michigan Territory continued under the jurisdiction of Bishop Fenwick at Cincinnati.

What Richard's personal feelings might have been regarding this blow he never revealed. He went on about his work as diligently as ever though his health was beginning to weaken.

Father Baraga had sent him a request from the north. He could use, he told Richard, "some small alphabets for the Indians." Richard supervised the printing of about a thousand such small alphabets and sent them to Baraga.

The only evidences of outward discouragement on Richard's part were the infrequent moments when he talked of leaving Detroit and going to L'Arbre Croche to finish his life in the midst of the Ottawa Indians who were especially dear to him.

Richard never did receive his appointment as Bishop of the Michigan diocese.

CHAPTER 19

EPIDEMIC

Since the end of the War of 1812, only small skir-
mishes had disturbed the peace between Indian and
white man. Now, in 1832, the tom-toms of war were
again being heard.

On the Iowa bank of the Mississippi River, Black
Hawk, war chief of the Sauk and Fox Indians, had
massed some five hundred warriors for an attack on
the white settlers of Illinois. Black Hawk, an old
friend of Chief Tecumseh, had fought on the side of
the British. He was angry at being forced to leave his
tribal lands on the Illinois side of the Mississippi and

167

was determined to retrieve them and wipe out all the whites in the Northwest Territory.

The still young United States had learned its lesson and was not to be caught napping with the threat of another bloody Indian war exploding along its frontier. Each of the states and territories in the "heartland" prepared for war, Michigan among them. The militia was activated, and all were ready to put down any uprising in the shortest possible time.

The federal government, meanwhile, dispatched troops to reinforce the garrisons in the frontier outposts. From the east, they came to Buffalo and by lake steamers were to be sent around to Chicago. One such transport, the *Henry Clay*, docked at Detroit to take on fuel and supplies on July 4, 1832.

As the steamer prepared to leave for Chicago, one of the soldiers on board became sick. In a few hours he was dead. Other soldiers were taken ill. The ship's doctor named the cause as the dreaded Asiatic cholera. Terrified, he deserted the *Henry Clay*.

Detroit authorities ordered the ship to leave the dock immediately. The captain moved it up the river a short distance and anchored. The situation became worse. More soldiers were infected. More died. The captain ordered the remaining soldiers to leave the ship which was now infested with disease.

168

The soldiers went ashore, many dying as they made their way back into Detroit. One hundred and fifty of the soldiers made it back into the city. The disease came with them.

In a few days, the sickness had spread like wildfire through all Detroit. Some citizens fled from Detroit to the north and south and west, anywhere to escape the spread of the disease.

But the news had gone before them. The people in the villages away from Detroit had already set up road blocks. With drawn guns, they ordered the Detroiters to go back home.

There was little that could be done to stem the high tide of the disease. There were only about a half dozen doctors in Detroit, and they worked night and day doing what they could.

In the turmoil and excitement, Father Gabriel Richard took charge of the few civilians who, though frightened, tried to remain calm. He organized them into a nursing group. Through his efforts, the state capitol building was quickly turned into a hospital and, for many days, Richard spent almost every hour in that building.

He had forgotten the weakening of his own health. He was too busy ministering to his people. Every ounce of his energy was given to nursing those who were sick, consoling those who lost a loved one, giving comfort to the dying, and burying those who died.

Everything possible was being done to stop the spread of the disease. The doctors issued warnings to the citizens not to eat fresh fruits or vegetables and to refrain from contact with other persons at all times. Richard impressed on everyone he saw the importance of following the orders of the medical authorities to the minutest detail.

The very air in Detroit was believed to be laden with the dreaded germs. To purify the air, all sorts of means were tried. Tar was burned in the streets. Sulphur was also used.

For about a month and a half the disease spread almost unabated through Detroit and the surrounding area. There is no true estimate of the number of deaths since the city newspaper, for fear it might panic the people even further, never published statistics.

In Richard's own papers, there is a report that "since July 6 there have been 51 deaths, nearly all from cholera, in my parish St. Anne alone." The report was not dated so it is impossible to estimate what period this represents from July 6, the second day after the *Henry Clay* docked on the waterfront.

Richard's efforts and his tireless work during this siege can never be minimized. What the city would have done without him is beyond thinking. A Detroiter named Roberts later painted a graphic picture of the priest during a discussion of the epidemic.

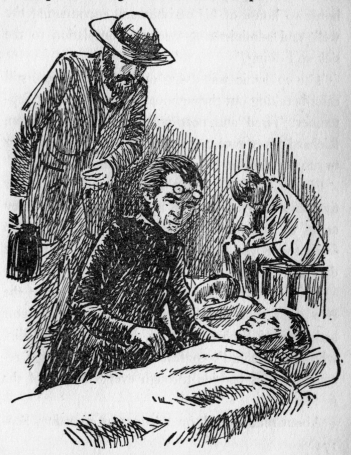

The plague raged for two months.

"During all the excitement and consternation for two months after its appearance here, Gabriel Richard might be seen clothed in the robes of his high calling, pale and emaciated, with spectacles on his forehead and prayer book in his hand, going from house to house of his parishioners, encouraging the well, and administering spiritual consolation to the sick and dying."

The epidemic was dying out but there were still cases breaking out throughout August and early September. Tired and near collapse from exhaustion, Richard never gave up even though he was beginning to suspect that he, himself, had caught the disease.

Finally he was stricken and ordered to bed. For five days his friends stood by him doing what they could to ease his pain. Father Badin had come up from the River Raisin. Frederic Baraga had come down from the northern country.

Faithfully, each half-hour, one or the other of the two priests would administer the medicine the doctor had ordered Richard to take. Either Father Badin, who was Richard's confessor, or Father Baraga remained at his bedside through every minute of the five days.

About nine o'clock on Wednesday morning, September 12, as Father Badin was about ready to begin Mass, he was quickly called to Richard's bedside. Father Baraga was afraid that the end was near.

Father Badin administered the sacrament of Extreme Unction and heard Richard mutter in Latin: "Now, oh Lord, let Thy servant depart in peace according to Thy word."

These were the last words known to have been spoken by Richard. As Father Badin completed the last rites, Richard became delirious, and all but unconscious. At ten minutes past three the following morning, Thursday, September 13, 1832, Gabriel Richard was dead at the age of sixty-five.

For one week his body lay in state before the altar of his beloved St. Anne's. From an early hour each morning to a later hour at night a constant stream of humanity passed by the thin, emaciated figure dressed in the robes of a simple missionary priest. Red man and white, Catholic and Protestant, the exalted official and the farmer, and the rich and the poor paid their last respects to the man who had left his mark on the frontier of the new nation.

The Thursday following Richard's death a solemn requiem Mass was sung for Gabriel Richard. Frederic Baraga gave the eulogy and, with Father Badin, led the procession which carried his body to the burial ground north of St. Anne's. Every bell in Detroit tolled the passing of its greatest citizen. More than two thousand people were in attendance as Gabriel Richard's remains were committed to the earth and into the custody of the Master he had served, as priest and missionary, through a lifetime of hardship and disappointment.

CHAPTER **20**

"RESURGET CINERIBUS"

Late on Tuesday, June 11, 1805, as he looked over the desolation left by the great fire which had leveled Detroit, Gabriel Richard spoke the words which are now indelibly etched in the city's history.

"Speramus meliora; resurget cineribus."

"We hope for better things; it will rise from its ashes."

Early that same morning he had felt bitterly hurt and discouraged by his failures and was ready to leave

175

Father Gabriel Richard: builder of Detroit

Detroit forever. But he remained through almost thirty more years of added disillusionment and suffering.

The village on the straits has, indeed, risen from its ashes. It is now one of the great cities of the world. And it has not forgotten the humble French priest who came into its old stockade from the Illinois country.

Wherever one may travel in metropolitan Detroit are evidences of the city's affection for Gabriel Richard. A park, two schools, and a library are named for him. Two statues of him have prominent locations within the city. There is hardly a child in any of its schools who cannot tell what Gabriel Richard means to Detroit.

Yet Richard considered himself a failure.

Historians agree that his life might be described as one seeming failure following another. But, they point out, each disappointment Richard endured merely proved how far he was ahead of his time.

Gabriel Richard believed in people and in the rights of people. He fought to preserve those rights, to make them understood by everybody so that no one might be denied them.

It was Richard's belief that no country, no city, was composed of buildings, of stone or mortar or lumber. It is human flesh, the people, who are a country or a city.

He came into an area which was wilderness. The people in the area were not white or red. They were not French or English. They were not Catholic or Protestant. They were but God's children, all alike.

Year after year he was the only one in a wide, vast area who could keep alive the principles of Christianity. To Catholic and non-Catholic, to Christian and non-Christian, he talked, always careful not to offend. It was not easy, for then, as now, there was much prejudice and lack of understanding.

In this most important work Gabriel Richard was certainly no failure. The expressions of tribute by almost every official of city, state, or national government with whom he came in contact are evidence enough. Few of these were of the Catholic faith. And few were there who did not have the highest praise for Father Gabriel Richard.

For Detroit and its people there are no words which can adequately express what he has meant. Without him there might not now be a Detroit.

If Antoine de la Mothe Cadillac was the founder of the city, then Gabriel Richard was its builder.

AUTHOR'S NOTE

Father Gabriel Richard's influence on the history and culture of Detroit, Michigan, and on most of the Northwest Territory is familiar to a majority of Midwesterners. Yet, though he was of the greatest significance in helping to civilize the entire early American frontier, few people removed from the Midwest are familiar with his name.

As a Sulpician, Gabriel Richard was a devoted priest, though often misunderstood and sometimes maligned. The reason, perhaps, was that he was far ahead of his time. He was certainly the first of his age to show the ecumenical spirit which is only today taking a firm hold throughout the world.

His prime interest was his people. Whatever he did, whatever he said, bore directly on the welfare, physical as well as spiritual, of his congregation.

Detroit was a small frontier village enclosed by a palisade when Richard first arrived. Its thinking and its future seemed no broader than the limits of the fort. The majority of the people in Richard's care as parish priest were uneducated and rough, and understood little or no English.

To hasten their development he furthered the establishment of schools and brought what must have been the first printing press into the territory. He published Michigan's first newspaper and printed and published its first books.

When he had taken care of his French parishioners he turned his attention to the plight of the Indians; he established missions and schools for them and fought for their fair treatment. American Indian policy was radically changed because of Gabriel Richard.

The basic situations in this story of Gabriel Richard are factual, though the author has taken some liberties in developing the situations and the spoken words.

Reading and culling information from articles, pamphlets, books, and notes was a lengthy affair. I would be most ungrateful if I were not to acknowledge the invaluable help given me by my young friend, Ted Dudek, who not only gathered much of the material but also spent long hours diligently typing the finished manuscript.

My heartfelt thanks must go to Barbara Lanigan for her advice and her patience.

And let me not forget another good friend, Father Edmund Schwager, to whom this book is dedicated. Without his gentle persuasion when a prod to work was needed, without his words of encouragement, the book might never have gone beyond the first chapter.

FURTHER READING

Catlin, George B. *The Story of Detroit*. Detroit, Michigan: Wayne University Press, 1926.

Woodford, Frank B., and Albert Hyma. *Gabriel Richard: Frontier Ambassador*. Detroit, Michigan: Wayne State University Press, 1958.

Work Projects Administration. *Michigan, a Guide to the Wolverine State*. New York: Oxford University Press, 1941.

INDEX

THE AUTHOR AND HIS BOOK

DAVID J. ABODAHER *grew up in Detroit, Gabriel Richard's city. After graduating from St. Vincent's High School, he went on to the University of Detroit. In his freshman year his first novelette was published, and in the next three years, at Notre Dame, he paid a large share of his college costs with his earnings as a radio writer. He left college in his senior year to write full time for radio, and in the following years he wrote several network series, and mystery and western programs including some episodes for the "Lone Ranger." He has published many short stories and articles in* The Detective Story Magazine, Baseball Magazine, *and the* Saturday Evening Post, *among others.*

After two years in the Signal Corps during World War II Mr. Abodaher returned to Detroit and entered the field of radio advertising. He has also written, directed and produced promotional movies. After many years as a free-lance writer, working for the Ford Motor Company, he recently joined the J. Walter Thompson advertising agency as a staff writer. His biography of Daniel Duluth is scheduled for publication next year. Mr. Abodaher is married and has a teen-age daughter.

UNDER THREE FLAGS (*Hawthorn, 1965*) *was designed by Stefan Salter and completely manufactured by American Book–Stratford Press. The body type is Linotype Janson, based on the letters of Anton Janson, a Dutch punchcutter who worked between 1660 and 1687.*

A HAWTHORN BOOK

HAWTHORN JUNIOR BIOGRAPHIES

Operation Escape: The Adventure of Father O'Flaherty, by Daniel Madden

To Far Places: The Story of Francis X. Ford, by Eva K. Betz

The Lion of Poland: The Story of Paderewski, by Ruth and Paul Hume

The Conscience of a King: The Story of Thomas More, by Margaret Stanley-Wrench

Pen and Bayonet: The Story of Joyce Kilmer, by Norah Smaridge

The Man Who Found Out Why: The Story of Gregor Mendel, by Gary Webster

The Tall American: The Story of Gary Cooper, by Richard Gehman

Wings of an Eagle: The Story of Michelangelo, by Anne M. Peck with Frank and Dorothy Getlein

The Door of Hope: The Story of Katharine Drexel, by Katherine Burton

Fire of Freedom: The Story of Col. Carlos Castillo Armas, by Jack Steffan

Doctor America: The Story of Tom Dooley, by Terry Morris

The Sea Tiger: The Story of Pedro Menéndez, by Frank Kolars

The First Californian: The Story of Fray Junípero Serra, by Donald Demarest

Wilderness Explorer: The Story of Samuel de Champlain, by Charles Morrow Wilson

Forked Lightning: The Story of General Philip H. Sheridan, by Albert Orbaan

The Hammer of Gaul: The Story of Charles Martel, by
  Shane Miller
Dawn from the West: The Story of Genevieve Caulfield,
  by Margaret Rau
Journey into Light: The Story of Louis Braille, by Gary
  Webster
*Monuments to Glory: The Story of Antonio Barluzzi,
  Architect of the Holy Land,* by Daniel Madden
The Crusader: The Story of Richard the Lionheart, by
  Alma Power-Waters
The King of Song: The Story of John McCormack, by
  Ruth and Paul Hume
Teller of Tales: The Story of Geoffrey Chaucer, by
  Margaret Stanley-Wrench
The Light Within: The Story of Maria Montessori, by
  Norah Smaridge